START ENJOYING YOUR CHILDREN AND STOP WORRYING!

"I suspect that after the first million or so mothers have read the book the sigh of relief may be loud enough to be heard across the land, accompanied by very welcome and urgently needed laughter.

"Lest it be overlooked in the pure pleasure of reading this volume, Dr. Gersh is a first-rate pediatrician practicing his craft with obvious relish and high intelligence. Several members of this department have already suggested that 'Gersh' be made required reading for our students, interns, and residents."

—DR. IRVING SCHULMAN,
    Professor and Head of the Department
    of Pediatrics, University of Illinois
    Medical Center, Chicago

How To Raise Children At Home In Your Spare Time

Marvin J. Gersh, M.D.

A FAWCETT CREST BOOK
Fawcett Publications, Inc., Greenwich, Conn.

To A. J. G., my first pediatrician,
to M. M. G., my present one,
and to my fellow workers
in child maintenance and repair.

CONTENTS

How To Raise
Children At Home
In Your Spare Time

WILL THE REAL DR. SPOCK
PLEASE STAND UP?

This age has been referred to as the age of the common man. It is more properly, in my judgment, the age of the unusual child. Practically no family is without one or more.

The need of guidance for the perplexed parent in raising unusual children has been met only partially by experts throughout the ages. In the beginning, child-raising experts warned that each child was an incipient devil. It was assumed that each child was basically sinful and that only through severity and discipline of the harshest sort could the little monsters be made to conform. The accent then was on prevention of spoiling the child.

The ubiquitous pendulum has made its inevitable swing, and the accent now, with most modern parents, is on the prevention of frustration. How, they cry out, can we spare our child traumatic experiences? How can we prevent sibling rivalry? How can we accomplish toilet-training without causing neurosis? How can we keep homes habitable without spanking the child?

This type of thinking, of course, has resulted in the era of permissiveness—which the experts, who led the way in the first place, are now busily trying to extricate us from.

Why then should another book be written on the subject when already the harassed parent has more literature on it that he can handle without confusion? The answer, gentle reader, is that much of this vast amount of information misses the mark. Perhaps the following letters will throw some light on the subject.

WHILE I HAVE YOU, DOCTOR*

Mrs. M. A. Aderbigbe, Rhodesia, writes:

Dear Doctor:
  Through the kindness of the L. F. U. (Libraries for the Underprivileged), I have read several of the most popular American baby books. I notice that most of your doctors recommend that parents and children sleep in separate chambers. One of these books states that the noise of intercourse may frighten little boys and give them a complex and may affect them later in life, particularly in their attitudes toward sex. Our quarters here in Bulawayo consist of one room, and naturally we all sleep in it. My husband and I were brought up in the same fashion. It hasn't given my husband a complex about sex. Sometimes I wish it would have. My son seems even less affected. He seems to laugh about it and often tries to imitate adults in the sex act. Actually we thought it was sort of funny. What does it all mean? And what is an Oedipus complex?

Dear Mrs. Aderbigbe:
  Thank you so much for writing. I can see how it would be difficult for you to arrange separate rooms. You needn't worry that things have turned out so well and that your practice of communal sleeping hasn't caused any phobias. We are not sure that all of this is true anyway, but we just like to worry about things like that. As for the Oedipus complex, it is based on a Greek myth about a boy who slew his father and married his mother. It has now become a well-established American myth.

Mrs. A. W. Kakula, British Guiana, writes:

Dear Doctor:
  I have read in a well-known American baby book that all two-year-olds are devils and it's a stage they

* Regrettably, every question asked by mothers in this book has actually been asked of me in my medical practice.

go through. It further states that they have temper tantrums, stubbornness, are given to saying no, and won't ever mind. This stage is passed through by age three. Well, I've had eight children that I can assure you were brought up like typical healthy British Guianese, and except for Esmail, now seventeen, who is still temperamental, stubborn, and contrary, I can't really say that the others did as the book suggests. Could it be that we are all abnormal?

Dear Mrs. Kakula:

Thank you so much for writing. It is always wonderful to hear from someone from British Guiana.

I am not so sure that your experience is so unusual, even for the United States. I think that we are beginning to find out what you have already discovered. Stages in the development of a child are not as real as people who write books like to think they are. Someone ought to write a book called *The Myth of the Terrible Two*. In the first place, it is the individual temperamental traits that are far more important than the so-called developmental stages that children are supposed to go through. A lot of it in this country is self-fulfilling prophecy.

In your ignorance, you probably didn't anticipate bad behavior from your children, and they didn't behave that way. We are taught to expect it; so we act as if it were to take place, and, lo and behold, it does.

Too, a lot of negativism—saying no—is learned. After all, when one of our children starts to walk we have to keep him from touching things. Our houses are full of breakable things, ash trays, antiques, lamps, bric-a-brac, high-fi sets, T. V.'s, all of which the child is not allowed to touch. It doesn't matter how curious he is.

One time a mother living in such a home complained about her two-year-old daughter. "She always says no. No matter what I ask her to do she says no." I asked this mother to go home and count the number of times she said no to her two-year-old. She called the next day and said, "After 154 times I stopped counting."

You see, Mrs. Kakula, we are having trouble adjusting to the material world that we have created, and we prefer to think that our children are going through inevitable predetermined stages. How about writing a book for us?

Mrs. Ada Mantinoma of Throggs Neck, New York, writes:

Dear Doctor:

I am having trouble with my eighteen-year-old boy, Melvin. Melvin used to be a good boy, but lately he has given me a lot of aggravation. He demanded money from me for marijuana cigarettes. He sits in his room sniffing glue. When I holler at him, he says everyone in Throggs Neck smokes marijuana and sniffs glue. I know he is lying. I think he may have gotten a girl in trouble, if you know what I mean. I can't understand it. Could it be his teeth?

Dear Mrs. Mantinoma:

As a rule doctors don't believe that any symptoms other than discomfort arise from teething. People have attributed fevers, diarrhea, convulsions, and mood disturbances to teething, but there is no proof that I know of that teething lies at the root of all these problems. I will have to admit that I have occasionally seen babies who have diarrhea or develop a rash with the eruption of each new tooth, but it is best not to make this assumption and to look for other causes.

As for Melvin, you mentioned that he was eighteen years old. It is true that his wisdom teeth are erupting, but if the ancients were correct, this should make Melvin more prudent, rather than reckless. I suggest you and Melvin's dad have a good heart-to-heart talk with Melvin. Let him know you are worried and see if that does any good. Should Melvin not appear moved, I would suggest that something is bothering him to make him act that way, and it may be wise for you to consult your family physician or your spiritual adviser, or your local guidance clinic or a private psychiatrist or some youth organization or perhaps all of these. You may find out that it is a stage that many youngsters go through in "trying to make the scene."

Mrs. P. W. Wedgewood of Lima, Ohio, writes:

Dear Doctor:
   Could a chiffonier toppling over on the foot of a one-year-old break it?

Dear Mrs. Wedgewood:
   It is always nice hearing from someone in Lima, Ohio. Your theoretical question poses some further questions to me. By "break it" I presume you mean the foot and not the chiffonier. I presume the one-year-old to whom you have referred is a human infant and quite possibly your own. Am I right so far? Next, some chiffoniers have mirrors placed on top of them which add to their weight. You did not mention broken glass or cuts; so I presume your chiffonier does not have a mirror.
   I'll have to admit that a chiffonier falling on the foot of a one-year-old could break the foot. I hope by the time this letter reaches you, you have had the good sense to have taken your baby to a doctor for an X-ray.

Mrs. Rai M. Chowdhury, Calcutta, India, writes:

Dear Doctor:
   I have been disturbed to read in one of your baby and child manuals that a child can only be expected to be healthy if he eats a serving of meat once a day. Naturally I want to do the best for my children, but I have some problems in that regard. As you know, some Hindu sects do not permit the eating of meat. In addition, even if I were to abandon this custom, I could not get meat for my children more than once a week. Fortunately my husband is a civil servant, and we can afford lots of vegetables, including beans. My children seem very healthy. Need I worry?

Dear Mrs. Chowdhury:
   Thanks so much for writing. I can assure you that you need not worry. In our country we produce so much meat that doctors think they have to help get rid of it. I, myself, have known several families who

do not eat meat, nor drink milk, nor eat eggs for that matter. They are not Hindus, but very strict vegetarians. America is full of people on exotic diets. I have found that children of such families are very healthy. They are not any healthier than other children who do eat meat, but they are certainly no less so. As long as one gets sufficient protein, and beans can supply the protein requirements, and calcium, which can be obtained from vegetables—carrots are full of calcium —you don't have to eat meat—or drink milk for that matter. It would be a good idea if we ate meat three times a week and sent the rest overseas.

Mrs. A. B. Frankel, Scranton, Pennsylvania, writes:

Dear Doctor:
   My thirteen-year-old son is very short for his age. Is there anything that I can do to make him grow? He is also very sensitive about his height. I have tried not to make him self-conscious about it and have encouraged him to talk about it. I have asked him many times, "Shorty, why are you so sensitive?" But he refuses to talk to me.

Dear Mrs. Frankel:
   Thank you so much for writing. It is always wonderful to hear from somebody from Scranton. I presume your child is well and that your doctor has checked him over carefully. Most short stature is hereditary. You did not mention the height of either your husband or you. If you and your husband are of normal height, the chances are that your son will be too. At thirteen, boys are often smaller than girls of the same age. Perhaps that is why Shorty is so sensitive. The reason that girls are relatively taller at this age is that they mature earlier. I have a feeling that Shorty will shoot up when he begins to go through the glandular changes associated with adolescence. You may help him psychologically though by getting him to think of himself as a short giant rather than a tall midget. By the way, how about changing his nickname to Buddy?

Mrs. Dora P. Norris of Bloomington, Indiana, writes:

Dear Doctor:

I have a three-year-old boy who is very selfish. He won't share his toys, he won't help tidy up his room, he never offers chocolates we give him to his younger sister. Tell me, Doctor, do they outgrow selfishness?

Dear Mrs. Norris:

The question you ask is a very important one. I wish I could say that they do outgrow selfishness, but actually there is very little evidence that they do. People learn to disguise it, sometimes even to repress it, but I cannot say that they outgrow it.

Mrs. A. L. Lutenbacher, White Plains, New York, writes:

Dear Doctor:

Last night my husband and I went to our first parent-teacher conference at the nursery school. In discussing the way our children spent their day, our daughter's teacher explained that after the children removed their own coats, to which she attached great significance, "in terms of their growth" as she put it, they were then allowed to "gravitate to the area of their major interest." My husband and I did not know precisely what this meant. Would you please explain?

Dear Mrs. Lutenbacher:

I can understand your difficulty. The problem will become simpler for you if you realize that your child's teacher is speaking nursery-schoolese. "They were then allowed to gravitate to the area of their major interest" means the kids could do what they wanted while the teachers knocked off for coffee.

Lest you think that we doctors are know-it-alls, let me report the following interchange between patient and doctor.

PATIENT: Why does my baby suck his thumb?
DOCTOR: I don't know.
PATIENT: How come my baby's toenails are so soft? His brother's weren't that way.

DOCTOR: I don't know.
PATIENT: How come my baby doesn't like carrots?
DOCTOR: I don't know.
PATIENT: Do you mind me asking you all these questions?
DOCTOR: No, not at all. How else are you going to learn?

Moral: Doctors can help you learn about your baby,
but they don't know everything.

THE BATTERED PARENT SYNDROME

The American parent has been beleaguered by articles
on child-rearing, mostly written by maiden ladies on a
warm Sunday afternoon, he has been lectured on the importance of love and affection by young teachers, still
sweaty from the hockey fields of Vassar, and deluged with
articles by child experts, first urging him to be more permissive, then urging him to set limits. Lastly but not
leastly, he has been assaulted by his own children, who
challenge his traditional role as a parent.

A well-known psychiatrist used to say that his patients
complained that their parents did not love them. Now
most of his patients complain that their children do not
love them. Is it any wonder that few people in this country
want to grow up to be parents? There is a kind of paranoid
style in American child rearing. The parent is always suspect. If his child's nose runs, if he wheezes, if he does
poorly in math or is below average in daydreaming, his
parents are to blame.

Let us face it. We pediatricians are not blameless. Many
a poor mother has been blamed for an infant's colic when
she showed up tense and angry after two or three weeks of
sleepless nights. "You see," we would mutter to ourselves,
"it is parental anxiety that is causing this colic." Sometimes it was milk allergy or some sugar intolerance, but
the parent was hardly in a position to talk back.

The American parent is guilt-ridden and defensive. This
has resulted in a certain amount of hypocrisy. Let me illustrate: I was examining, with a medical student, a child
who was complaining of abdominal pain. After reviewing
the history, the medical student suggested the possibility
that this abdominal pain might have been emotional in origin. The mother, who was sophisticated in these matters

and who had had psychotherapy, picked this up immediately. "Doctor, I am sure it could not be emotional. I give her lots of love and affection." Now turning menacingly to her daughter, eyes wide, teeth bared, she demanded, "Don't I, Debbie?" Debbie agreed.

When anything goes wrong with a child, the parent is made to feel that he has not given his child enough love and affection. Of course no one is against a lot of love and affection. The point of the matter is that you cannot be forced to give it. Love arises out of a situation. You do not smear it on like butter on bread. Also remember, it is not a cure for all ills.

Child-rearing is so serious that no parent can afford to take it seriously.

HOW TO WEAN YOURSELF FROM BABY BOOKS

After you have had your third or fourth child, you are probably ready to start weaning yourself from baby books. Remember you are not going to succeed right away. It is a good idea to start trying to wean yourself little by little, beginning with your second child. Start with something simple.

Let us say that your baby has spit up a little bit. Naturally you will think back automatically to the section in your baby book on spitting up. You will remember that many babies spit up and that many babies do not, and that some babies spit up once in a while, and some babies spit up every day, and still there are some babies who spit up once in a while for a while and then spit up every day for a while.

You will immediately recognize that your baby is one of the many babies who spit up. It is too soon for you to know whether he is one of the once in a while spitters, or the daily spitters, or the once in a while sometimes daily spitters, or the daily double spitters.

Naturally most spitting up is not serious, but on the other hand, spitting up can be serious if it is not spitting up but it may appear to be spitting up, but actually it may be projectile vomiting, so the section says. Well, if it is projectile vomiting, it may be serious, but since most spitting up is not serious, it probably is not projectile vomiting, but on the other hand, if you are in doubt, you can always call up your pediatrician.

Try to be breezy and cheerful so that the baby does not get the idea that you are upset; after all if you are tense, baby may become tense, and this may cause the baby to spit up. Sometimes spitting up may be emotional, and in some cases it may mean that you are rejecting your baby. Remember we all have unconscious feelings that we do not know about. Sometimes we need the help of a child psychologist, or your local child guidance clinic. Suppose your town does not have a child guidance clinic, and you cannot afford a good child psychologist: try to manage as best you can, and remember a breezy, cheerful and confident attitude is always best. Be firm but try not to be harsh. Remember spitting up is O. K. If it shoots out a foot or two or if spitting up is associated with weight loss, then you should see your doctor. Otherwise, if your baby spits up, just DUCK.

I think you will learn to wean yourself from baby books when you see that sometimes the writer of the book is as scared as you are. His insecurity lies in the fact that he is afraid to reassure you completely lest he lead you to error. You will see in most books on child care that toward the end of each chapter or paragraph on a subject, the author will begin to hedge. He is getting a little insecure too. Consequently, he will almost always add, after reassuring you most of the way, that if there is any doubt you'd best call your doctor. He gets himself off the hook that way, and frankly I think it is unavoidable.

You cannot teach anybody to play golf by the book, much less raise a child by the book. I can see no way out for the parents, other than experience. I have found out that the number of questions asked by parents cuts down progressively as the number of children increases. By the second or third child, you can tell a serious problem from a trivial one. You are consulting your doctor regularly anyway, and things work out quite well. If only we could make our first baby seem like our second.

HOW TO TREAT YOUR
FIRST CHILD AS IF
IT WERE YOUR SECOND

"I used to worry so much about my first baby, I almost went crazy. I do not worry nearly so much about my second one. I do not pay half as much attention to him, and he seems to be doing better. If only I could have acted that way with my first."

The view this mother was expressing is quite common. Many first mothers go through a period of obsessional psychosis, which lasts about three months. It expresses itself in excessive preoccupation with normal events and slight variations that affect many babies. Every snort means pneumonia; every tiny rash, the plague; and every loose stool means diarrhea. I am afraid sometimes that we pediatricians aid and abet the mother. We do this by answering all her questions literally, which only results in more questions, then getting annoyed, which is mutually frustrating, or paying no attention at all and handing her a lot of forms or referring her to one baby book or another.

My own bias, I use the word bias since there is no known sure-fire method of handling this problem, is to try to provide the factual guide lines within which the mother may operate and then preach or teach that she must learn how to handle her own baby and learn to respond to him. The best approach in the first three months is to find out what the baby wants and then to let him have it. I admit there are exceptions as there are to all rules, and in another chapter I have warned against the possibility of becoming a slave to your baby. Most babies, however, can be handled very well if the mother will allow her own natural feminine receptivity to guide her as to the needs of the baby. All this is by way of a philosophical approach. Babies, like the world, need more changing than they do philosophy, so let me present you with some commonly encountered thoughts, problems, and questions that disturb parents of first babies.

WORRIES OF NEW PARENTS

What Will My New Baby Look Like?

I recall my first delivery when I was a medical student. I proudly held the infant in my extended arms toward the mother, my face turned in profile toward the window, to better catch the rays of the sun—like an oil painting I had once seen called "The Ages of a Physician." It was to be a dramatic moment. "He looks like a little monkey, doesn't he," said this mother of four. I was hurt. How could she talk about my baby that way. We had switched roles for that brief moment. This mother was the realist, I was not.

However, many mothers are disappointed with the appearance of their babies. My wife cried when the nurse handed her the baby and she saw her "little chicken legs" sticking out of her diaper. Real newborns do not look like the babies on the backs of cereal boxes. The skin may be frighteningly red, or unpleasantly blotchy. It may be cracked, dry, or peeling. It may be covered with fine downy black hair. In short, the baby may look barely humanoid.

I am not done yet. His head may be misshapen. Very often it is unnaturally elongated, with a kind of bony bun in the back, or there may be a distinct swelling on one or both sides of the head. To make matters worse, he may open only one eye. And should he at that moment pass a little gas, resulting in a kind of sardonic smile, the effect can be unnerving. There may be a discharge from both eyes as a result of medication administered at birth to prevent serious eye disease. His chin, as it is in many infants, may be underdeveloped, giving him an almost Andy Gump appearance.

His arms and legs are relatively short for his trunk. It is

of interest to note that painters of the Renaissance doing madonna and child paintings, probably for esthetic reasons, gave their infants childlike rather than baby proportions, making their arms and legs relatively longer in proportion to their trunks.

Sometimes there is a swelling around the eyes and even a slight swelling of the feet. His or her breast may be somewhat full and may even discharge milk. This is the result of the mother's hormones passing through the placenta and causing breast development in both male and female babies. It usually goes away in a matter of weeks.

The abdomen may be full and large and move prominently with respiration. The genitalia may cause you to be concerned. Sometimes the testicles appear somewhat large. Usually this is due to a collection of water in the sac surrounding the testicles, called a hydrocele, and it usually disappears. In girls the clitoris may seem enlarged because of transmitted hormones, but it regresses. In girls also a vaginal discharge may be noted.

Add to all this the presence of blue hands and feet, and your baby may not correspond to the image you had while you were carrying him.

I must admit that not all mothers react with disturbance to the physical appearance of their babies. Many mothers are so worried lest they give birth to a deformed child that they are relieved. In my description of the newborn, I may have laid it on a little thick, but now your actual, in contrast to your fantasied, first baby should not come as a shock.

How Come He Does Not Eat?

For the first two or three days, your baby may eat very little. He needs very little. Often, premature infants are purposely not fed for 48 hours or so because they might swallow the wrong way. There is no apparent adverse effect.

Why Is He Losing Weight?

It is very common for new babies to lose weight. As much as ten per cent of their body weight may be lost in the first ten days of life without it being considered abnormal.

He Won't Burp for Me.

Mothers often tell me this in hurt tones. It is as if a clash of wills were involved and the baby was refusing to burp out of sheer perversity. A baby may burp after taking a quarter of an ounce or three ounces. You will have to learn by his signs of discomfort, wriggling, grimacing, or crying, when and if he wants to burp. Some babies do not burp at all. "I have been trying to get him to burp for 27 minutes, and he still won't," one exasperated, obviously statistically-minded mother once told me. Actually if you keep the baby's head up as you feed him and then put him in a bassinet tilted so the head is held up, you may not have to burp him at all. It is a principle of physics that since gas is lighter than fluid, it will rise to the top. Gas causes discomfort only if it has to pass through the entire intestinal tract and out the rectum. Proper positioning by elevating the head of the crib or bassinet will in most instances correct this.

I Don't Mind Feeding Him, But What Do I Do About the Other End?

Yesterday he had four stools. Today he had three. How come?
A baby is not a machine. Even if he ate an exact amount each day, which seems unlikely, his digestive processes might vary.

He had a green movement. Should I panic? Contrary to what you may have read, an occasional green movement, or even an occasional loose stool, or an occasional green loose stool, is not a cause for concern.

If he does not have a bowel movement, won't he burst? Occasionally babies may go a whole day without a bowel movement. This is particularly true of breast-fed babies, some of whom have been known to go a whole week without having a bowel movement without adverse effect. The worst that occasional constipation can cause is a little discomfort. If it persists, there are many preparations your physician can advise you to use. It is never an emergency matter.

Why does he strain so much? Is he constipated? Infants between three and about ten weeks often strain while having a bowel movement, despite the fact that the stool is soft. This is due to the fact that the rectal sphincter, a muscular ring at the end of the intestinal tract, goes into spasm. This condition usually goes away spontaneously. Your doctor may want to do a rectal examination to see if the sphincter is tight.

What Is that Rash on His Face?—Which One?

Infants are often born with little whiteheads over the ridge on their noses. These are blocked oil glands, and they will go away without treatment in a couple of weeks. Infants also often have blotchy rashes on their faces for the first few months. They may be due to drooling, transient allergies, or rubbing against a sheet, particularly if it has been washed in a detergent. They are never serious and they go away without treatment. Sometimes infants are born with flat red "birthmarks" in the mid-forehead, extending toward the nose. These are dilated proliferated small blood vessels, or capillaries. They are also often seen on the eyelids, where they may be confused with some sort of irritation, or are present on the back of the neck. I have never seen one of these flat birthmarks on the face or the lids persist. Those on the back of the neck may, but they are usually covered by the hair line.

How Come His Belly Button Sticks Out So Much?

It is quite common for the navel to be prominent. In most instances this is due to a "skin type of cord," which means that the skin grows along the umbilical cord. When the cord falls off the skin is loose and folded on itself. This usually flattens out with age.

The second cause for prominence of the umbilicus is the umbilical hernia. Do not let the term hernia frighten you. It merely means—merely you say!—that part of the abdominal contents are protruding through a ring-like opening in the abdominal musculature. Such a hernia may vary from dime-sized to half-dollar-sized. On straining with laughing, crying, or stooling, the thing may look like it is going to pop, but they never do. Most of them close over spontaneously, even without treatment. Some doctors think that strapping may be of help; some don't. When the openings are larger than dime-sized, I have strapped them.

I have no way of proving statistically that it is helpful, but my impression is that it is.

I Am Afraid He Will Stop Breathing.

So-called "crib deaths," purportedly due to smothering, are an exceedingly rare type of accident, rarer than death by fire, for example. In addition, the cause of death in such cases, while not clearly established, is surely not due to smothering. Anaphylactic reactions—massive allergic response or overwhelming infections—have been suggested as possible causes. A baby who can raise his head while lying prone on a firm mattress will not smother. If there is any problem or doubt, keep him on his back.

How Come He Does Not Sleep?

Unfortunately many mothers have been led to believe that a baby will sleep in between feedings, waking up every few hours to take his full bottle and go back to sleep. It would be nice if it were true, but unfortunately such is not always the case. Infants vary in their sleep requirements as much as adults. I have seen babies who slept ten hours a day, and others who slept eighteen hours a day. I do not know why.

Do not assume that if your baby is not sleeping very much that you are doing something wrong. It may be his nature. I have rarely found that offering more food or the early introduction of solids has changed a baby's sleep pattern. I have even seen babies who gained weight poorly, indicating they were underfed, but who slept all the time. In some ways sleep patterns are independent of feeding patterns. The ability to sleep ten hours at a time, for example, may reflect a maturity of the sleep center, rather than a full stomach. In any event, no matter how much you feed an infant, the stomach empties in four hours.

Why Does He Cry All the Time?

The average baby cries about two hours a day. To a mother this may seem like an eternity, but it is nevertheless about 120 minutes. Sometimes the crying is sporadic during the day; sometimes the baby saves it all up for a particular period. If a baby cries incessantly, something must be wrong and it usually is not you. See the chapter, "For Crying Out Loud, What Is Colic?" There are occasional babies who cry predominantly at night. This has been referred to as night colic. I do not know the reason for this phenomenon, but antispasmodic in large doses may be helpful. If you have one of those night criers, you will try anything.

How Come His Legs Are Bowed?

Many babies appear to have bowlegs. The bowing is not at the knee, but in the shin bone. It is not related to early standing. No matter how bad a "tibia bowing" is, I have never seen a case which did not correct itself spontaneously.

Doctor, Have I Asked You All the Questions that I Am Supposed to Ask?

I know that there is no end of questions that you may want to ask. I am pretty sure that most doctors run out of answers before mothers run out of questions. As I have indicated at the start, it is amazing how the number of questions diminishes with each successive baby. I suppose that mothers become progressively less concerned with individual variations. They learn, as must we all, that by observing a baby, they can distinguish those signs with serious implications and those with none. They learn confidence through experience, because there is no other way. I shall end by quoting a mother of a two-month-old baby girl, who returned for her monthly visit much relieved. She even seemed triumphant. "I have figured it all out," she said. "I cannot tell her what to do. I have to figure out what she wants and then give it to her."

HOW TO CURE THE BABY BLUES

Many mothers feel blue after the birth of a baby. If this is severe enough it is referred to as a postpartum depression. One possible cure for this is the reintroduction of an old custom called "couvade."

Marco Polo first encountered couvade in southern Cathay. It still exists in parts of Spain and South America, where the incidence of postpartum depression is either low or unreported. Marco Polo makes no mention of baby blues.

As soon as a baby is born, the infant is washed and swathed. The mother then arises immediately from her bed and returns to her household duties. Simultaneously her husband climbs into the bed and remains there for several days with the new-born baby, to help "hatch" him.

The sight of a rising young IBM executive, removing his small brimmed felt, his gray flannels, and climbing into bed with his attache case to help hatch the baby, may help offset a mother's depression, if it does not kill her.

The practice of couvade may also be recommended as something for large companies to encourage as a sure cure for "executive fatigue." One may anticipate some difficulty in the modern hospital setup and at the present time I doubt if Blue Cross would go for it, but, who knows.

Let us say that neither your husband nor the hospital administration will permit couvade. Let's face it—they have problems too. Then what can be done about baby blues? I think it is helpful to know in the first place that this let-down feeling is quite common. There are many women who experience an enormous sense of well-being, called euphoria, during pregnancy. There are many factors involved in this, and surely, although it is not well understood, one of these is glandular. There is a great change in the glandular or hormonal pattern during pregnancy. After the birth of the baby there is again another change which I think has a great effect on the spirits of the mother. For this reason I find it hard to predict on the basis of the mother's personality who will get depressed and who won't. I am constantly surprised both ways.

Come to Me My Melancholy Mommy.

Talk about it. Do not be afraid to admit that you are feeling low. Don't feel that you have to put on a performance of the happy mother for all your visitors. Cry if you feel like it. Do not compound your depression with shame. You may feel as if you are in a room with no exit, that all you can see before you is a never-ending series of problems and responsibility. The world may look black, and you cannot see daylight. Understand that these feelings, no matter how strong, are irrational. There can and will be brighter days. You are a mother now. Great joys await you. Plan some fun. Say, for example, at the end of the week I am going to see a good movie. Try something light. Avoid movies like *The Birth of a Nation*. The symbolism may be overwhelming. Promise yourself a new dress, a night on the town. In any event, to avoid the feeling and the actuality of entrapment, get out of the house regularly once a week. Even if you are breast-feeding, a supplemental bottle once in a while will not harm the baby and will help you.

And Baby Makes Three.

I can remember a young Bohemian type who had her first baby. When I visited her, she proclaimed without my asking, "We are not going to let the baby change our lives at all." She had majored in arts in school. Her specialty was thirteenth-century Persian filigree, and pre-Inca pottery. I knew she was whistling in the dark, and this attitude would fail her. When you have a baby, a wise friend of mine once remarked, you make the greatest biological and psychological shift of your life; you go in an instant from being someone's child to being someone's parent. It is quite a change.

Father can get blue too. With fathers the causes are not, of course, physiological. A black-leather-jacket, long-sideburned type I once met, said rather frankly, "What do I need this all for. Before I was married I was making 150 bucks a week, I had my own 'Merc' [Mercury], I really had a ball."

It is a tribute to the perversity and the unpredictibility of man that the unpromising-looking young fellow became a devoted, helpful father. Perhaps it was his candor that helped. At least he saw the problem.

I do not want to add to your problems by pointing out that your husband may be just as affected and upset as you. I find this particularly true in fathers, for example, who wanted a boy and got a girl. Such a father may be terribly resentful, but he may not talk about it. It is helpful if you can communicate your feelings to him, and he can to you. I do not mean in an angry, whining way but merely as a statement of fact. You might say, "I feel depressed, I need you." You have to be prepared on another day to hear him say that to you. This sharing, this community of feelings, can be sustaining and can be the making of a very enduring and strong union.

HOW TO SOLVE
EATING PROBLEMS
NOW AND FOREVER

Most experts agree that children should be fed. Accepting the necessity of feeding, two important questions remain. When? and What?

I should like to write plainly about feeding—trying to make it simple, which it really is, so as to free mothers from excessive preoccupation and allow them to mother their children. Obviously what I am about to write is not going to be everybody's cup of tea, but for the mother who can retain her sense of proportion I think it will be helpful.

DOES HE HAVE A CLOCK IN HIS STOMACH?

As a rule, I recommend self-regulation. That is, feeding the baby when he is hungry. I would suggest feeding him before you retire, however, so that you can get some sleep. When a baby is two months old you may try skipping the night feeding and see how he does.

There is an occasional rare baby who never seems satisfied and the mother becomes a slave to him. If your baby does not develop a self-regulated pattern after one month, I suggest you yourself institute a schedule. You may have to let him cry, but that will not hurt. He will adjust to the schedule eventually.

The self-regulating method had its original impetus from the psychologically oriented pediatricians. Actually there is no evidence that the manner in which you feed your baby, breast or bottle, fixed schedule or permissive style, has any known long-range psychological effects. I can tell you from experience, however, that you will have a lot quieter house if you feed your baby when he is hungry.

DO YOU BELIEVE IN BREAST-FEEDING?

There has been a great deal of debate about the advantage and disadvantage of breast-feeding. The average mother is in need of some help in deciding whether she should or should not breast-feed.

All mothers should breast-feed their babies, except of course those mothers who shouldn't. The problem is primarily psychological. If a mother feels on a superficial level that she should, but on a deeper level that she shouldn't, then she shouldn't. If, on the other hand, she feels that she shouldn't when basically she knows that she should, then she should, providing that she knows on which level she is operating.

There are so many misconceptions about breast-feeding that I hardly know where to begin. It sounds logical to begin at the breast. It is generally agreed that the size of the breast is of no importance for feeding, but it is not generally well appreciated how important the shape of the breast is. Dr. Mavis Gunther, who spent several years observing mothers breast-feeding, was able to predict, simply by observing the shape of the breast, whether the infant would be able to feed effectively or not. She teaches that the "nipple is like a cherry on a stalk." The "cherry" nipple should not be grasped between the gums, but rather should go to the back of the mouth. When the nipple goes into the back of the mouth, it touches the tongue, the soft palate, and the tissues of the mouth. This seems to stimulate the infant to suck vigorously. When the nipple cannot be or is not so placed, the infant is apathetic and behaves as if he does not want the breast. It actually is not a question of wanting, or even a matter of taste; it is a complex reflex pattern independent of the good intentions of the mother.

The breast has three parts: the breast itself, the nipple and the areola. The areola is the red, dark area surrounding the nipple. Dr. Gunther found that the "protractility" of the areola was important. Protractility refers to the capacity of this tissue, when squeezed by the infant's jaws, to thrust the nipple forward. The nipple, thus thrust forward, causes the reflex pattern I have described to come into action, and successful feeding takes place. It all sounds so mechanical and unromantic, doesn't it?

Chance plays a role, too, in the success of breast-feeding. Dr. Gunther noted that there were infants who, when they started to feed, would struggle and seem to beat the breast with their fists. She noticed that this behavior was similar to that of babies who had had their oxygen supply cut off. That is precisely what happened to these babies. Either their upper lip or Mother's breast got pressed against the nose, making it difficult for the infant to breathe. If this happens two or three times without anyone realizing what is happening, the infant gets conditioned against the breast, and it may become practically impossible to get him to breast-feed.

Dr. Gunther noted, too, that brunettes seemed to be more successful at breast-feeding than fair-haired people. Blondes may have more fun, but not at breast-feeding.

So you see if you cannot breast-feed, there is no need to feel guilty or unmotherly or inadequate or whatever derogatory term you choose. It may be out of your control.

If all this is true, and modern woman is really not at fault, what did women in earlier times do? For one thing, they used wet nurses. Where this was not possible, all-glass bottles were used. What do primitive women do? They also use wet nurses if available. In some African communities, if the baby does not feed well from the breast, the mother puts her finger into the baby's mouth to make it swallow and then tips in the milk with the palm of her hand. It is a sure bet she does not sit in her hut analyzing herself.

Is Breast Best?

Breast milk is, of course, an excellent source of nutrition. It is not perfect, however, and must be supplemented by vitamins. It does not cause allergies as cow's milk might. It is also unlikely to be contaminated. Babies who are breast-fed seem to develop resistance to certain types of infection. Nevertheless, with the availability of a variety of formulas that can be used if allergy is to be prevented or alleviated, with good sterilization and refrigeration so that infection in bottle-fed babies is rare, with a wide variety of antibiotics available should infection arise, I do not think a case can be made for breast-feeding on a *physical* basis.

People often argue that breast-feeding is better from a psychological point of view. There is no evidence that breast-fed infants are psychologically different or emotionally more stable than bottle-fed infants. As a matter of fact, Dr. Robert Fredeen of Kansas has had mothers cup-feed babies for many years. Recent psychological studies done retrospectively on this group show no evidence of emotional disturbance as a result.

If Your Doctor Had Breasts, What Would He Do?

I have stressed the mechanical and physical factors in breast-feeding because I feel that they have received insufficient attention. We have tended to feel that if breast-feeding did not work out, it was due to some fault of the mother's. It is commonly said, "She is too tense," or "She is not motherly," or the worst charge of all, "She is rejecting her baby." As a consequence of this attitude, many mothers have been made to feel guilty about their inability to breast-feed. It is very unfair.

I am not denying that motivation does play a role in whether a mother will even try to breast-feed or, if she does, whether it will be successful. In many instances the mother's attitude has been determined long before she had a baby. The sources of an anti-breast-feeding attitude can be found in the individual history of the mother and in the cultural patterns of the community. In a recent study it was found that there was a direct correlation between playing with dolls in childhood and the desire to breast-feed. This should be fairly obvious because girls who have always had a high interest in mothering might be able to accept the idea of breast-feeding better than little girls who played baseball, for example. I do not mean that there is cause and effect here, nor do I mean to suggest that if you buy a lot of dolls, your daughters are more apt to breast-feed. I am simply trying to cite an example to show that a particular attitude may be formed early. I am not even saying the attitude cannot be changed.

Cultural phenomena are equally important. In any society where substitutes for mother's milk are readily available, where good sterilization techniques are easy to perform and refrigeration is accessible to everyone, there has been a decline in breast-feeding. This decline has probably been somewhat slowed by exhortation from the medical community; but, nevertheless, bottle-feeding is increasing not only in the United States but throughout the world. It may be said that one of the technological displacements caused by the industrial revolution was the human breast.

Temporarily related to the displacement of the breast as a source of nutrition has been its simultaneous rise as a sex symbol. Once used primarily to nurture the young, it is now used by girls as a weapon to win men. It is factually true that in any culture where the breast has become a sex symbol breast-feeding has declined. This new status of the breast has had a snow-balling effect on bottle-feeding because a young lady aware of the sexuality of the breast is less likely to be willing to expose one for feeding purposes—even in front of her husband. Anyway, that is what the sociologists say.

To sum up, you have the right to choose whether you want to breast-feed or not. There is no phychological advantage to breast-feeding that has ever been consistently demonstrated. You have not deprived your infant of his birthright if you don't breast-feed. The physical advantages of breast-feeding in our society, though present, are so readily overcome that I do not feel that they are significant in helping you make up your mind.

If you do not want to breast-feed, you needn't feel guilty. If you try it and it doesn't work out, it is probably due to factors beyond your control. One word of warning. For reasons that I will let the reader fantasize about, the most enthusiastic advocates of breast-feeding are not mothers, not grandmothers, not nurses, but male pediatricians. During a discussion with a slightly obese male pediatrician who was urging breast-feeding with great enthusiasm, I found my eyes somewhat unaccountably fixed on his shirt front. People who do not wear bras should not insist on breast-feeding.

HITTING THE BOTTLE AT AN EARLY AGE

Let us say that with or without advice, you have decided to bottle-feed your baby. The first thing to remember is always to hold the baby when you are feeding him. Most psychologists feel that bodily contact is an important stimulus to secure emotional growth. Never prop the baby's bottle. An infant can choke on it since he has no way of stopping the flow. We shall now talk about formulas.

You can choose from: whole milk, evaporated milk, and soy bean milk meat base formula; Olac, Similac, Bremil, Alacta, S. M. A., powdered or liquid form, Varramel Lactum, Meyergartners Milsch (a German product), Le Mans Lait (a French product), and a recently developed whales milk. (Some mothers, faced with the choice between all these products, are unable to make a decision and conclude that breast-feeding nature's own formula may be the simplest procedure after all.)

All formulas are based on the principle of imitating mother's milk, in terms of protein, fat, carbohydrates. If we wish to make a formula from cow's milk for example, we must modify it to resemble mother's milk. Cow's milk contains more protein than mother's milk; therefore, we add water to reduce the amount of protein. Cow's milk contains less sugar; therefore, we must add sugar. The fat content in mother's and cow's milk is roughly equal.

A mother may make up her own formula, consisting of milk, water and sugar, or she may buy a ready-made one, consisting of milk, water, and sugar. The ready-made ones usually have vitamins added by the maker. They also usually have the butter fat removed and replaced with equally nutritious, less expensive vegetable oils. The manufacturers profit from this, baby does not suffer, and everyone is usually happy. There are a great variety of formulas available. Please remember that they are all based on the same principle. Frankly, there is not much difference between them. There is no question but that ninety-five per cent of babies can take any sort of formula. The five per cent who have ninety-five per cent of the problems with formulas I shall discuss later.

Many mothers are too prone to change formulas. If a baby burps, spits up, or has an occasional loose stool, right away they want to change the formula. Personally I would rather fight than switch. I resist switching because usually what the mothers complain of has nothing to do with formulas.

The following formula can be given to any baby from birth to three months of age. It is made with:

- 1 can evaporated milk (13 ounces)
- 17 ounces of water
- 2 tablespoons of table sugar or light Karo syrup.

You don't have to be a chemist to make the mixture. Actually, accurate measuring is not necessary. The formula can be prepared by getting a quart bottle, pouring in one can of evaporated milk, adding two tablespoons of sugar or light Karo syrup, and filling with water to the top. *Voilà*, it is made. The only variable is the amount you give the child at any one feeding. You may have to increase the *amount* from four to six to eight ounces per bottle, but proportions of the formula remain the same. I call this formula a Mother Bloor's old-fashioned.

If you have trouble getting your husband to help make this formula, you can encourage him to do so by getting hold of a quart martini pitcher. He adds the can of evaporated milk, adds the sugar or light Karo syrup, fills water to the top, takes two steps backward and shouts, "vermouth." He stirs the pitcher gently so as not to bruise the preparation. You had best check him the first two or three times, to make sure that he has not added an olive or lemon peel.

If you should decide to use any of the proprietary preparations with directions on the can, that is fine too. Let me emphasize that there is little difference between one or the other. With most proprietary formulas no additional vitamins are needed. The vitamin content is listed on the can. Ready-made formulas in bottles are also available. They are quite expensive. They may be used, however, as relief bottles or, of course, if economy is no problem.

Is Sterilization Necessary?

There is some question as to whether sterilization is necessary or indeed under certain circumstances whether it is effective. At the present time if you insist on making the whole day's formula at once, it probably is best to sterilize, either by the aseptic technique or the terminal sterilization method.

A method which I believe to be preferable to either method because of its speed and safety is the "one at a time" method. Here is how it goes:

1. Wash your hands with soap and water.

2. Wash the bottle, nipple, funnel, and can opener with soap or detergent and water. A dish washer is fine but not necessary.

3. For a full-strength formula that can be used for any baby after birth, first add three ounces of tap water (warm or cold) and one teaspoonful—repeat teaspoonful—of light Karo syrup or table sugar to the bottle. If sugar is used, swirl the mixture around to dissolve the sugar.

4. Wash off the top of the can of evaporated milk with soap and running water. With a clean can opener, make two holes in the can. Pour two ounces of milk into the bottle with the water and sugar or Karo. Notice that the proportion of water to milk is three to two. If you wish to make up more, keep roughly to the same proportions. For eight ounces of formula, five ounces of water, three ounces of milk, and one teaspoonful of light Karo syrup or table sugar will do fine without having to use a computer.

If you decide to buy a ready-made preparation, you follow steps 1 and 2 above to get your hands and the equipment clean. Then add formula and water in the proportions indicated by your doctor or the manufacturers. This applies either to liquid preparations, where the proportions are usually one ounce of prepared concentrated formula to one ounce of water, or, if powder, one measure of powder to two ounces of water.

Place the unused portion of the evaporated milk or liquid formula in the refrigerator immediately, until needed for the next feeding.

5. Place the nipple on the bottle and feed immediately. Notice that tap water has been used and that warming is not necessary (see the section below on warming).

6. After baby has finished with the bottle, discard any remaining formula and rinse the bottle and nipple in running water, making sure the nipple holes are clean and remembering to remove curds that may get stuck in the bottom of the bottle.

Although there are six steps to follow, this method is very quick. When baby begins to get hungry you can prepare a bottle faster than you can say Dr. Spock. It all boils down to the fact that sterilization and heating are not necessary.

Another advantage to this method is that since the formula is prepared for immediate use, it does not stand around and have a chance to become contaminated. The biggest danger in formula feeding comes from giving an infant part of a bottle, letting it stand around for an hour or so, and then giving him the rest of it. It is standing at room temperature that causes contamination. This goes, too, for formulas prepared by terminal sterilization.

Terminal Sterilization

If for one reason or other, either because you are not using pasteurized milk, or because you are using well or spring water, or because of the lack of availability of good refrigeration, or because you are "chicken," or your doctor insists on it, you decide in favor of sterilization, then I would recommend the terminal method of sterilization.

In any event, after three months I recommend switching to whole milk and stopping sterilization.

For terminal sterilization, mix formula as on page 40. Pour into bottles, place nipples upside down on bottles, and screw caps on lightly. Place bottles in a pan deep enough to hold the bottles standing up (if you have a regular sterilizer there will be a rack to hold the bottles, but this is not necessary). Put one to two inches of water in the bottom of the pan, cover, and bring to a boil. Let boil for 25 minutes. Remove from heat and let cool to lukewarm before refrigerating.

Is Warming a Bottle Necessary?

You probably have always thought that warming the bottle is necessary. However, doctors at Bellevue Hospital in New York fed premature babies, the frailest of all infants, with ice-cold formulas without adverse effect. Other physicians and hospitals have done this, too, as routine, and it has worked out fine. I must admit that many mothers find the idea of serving ice-cold formulas to babies repugnant. I suspect they associate maternal warmth with warm formulas and feel they would be considered cold or rejecting serving a chilled formula. It will take some time to get over this. Actually the stomach is filled with warm gastric juices, and the formula is quickly warmed or cooled to body temperature after it enters the stomach.

The Consistency of the Formula

Is there a relationship between the consistency of the formula and personality?

There is an apocryphal story that some years ago a man named Gerstman attempted to show a correlation between the personality of the child and the consistency of the formula. He reasoned that if the formula contained small lumps of curdled milk, the infant would be exposed too soon to the inconsistency of his environment. He might grow up marked by a predisposition to expect unexpected lumps and bumps in life. This might tend to make him wary, suspicious, and pessimistic. This work was discredited when it was found out that Gerstman, who exhibited all the traits of the so-called "lumpy personality of Gerstman," had been breast-fed.

The important thing to remember is that after preparing a formula by sterilization, one should allow it to cool at room temperature for a few minutes before placing it in the refrigerator. In this way the milk will not curdle or clog the nipple holes.

Nipple Holes

Before our knowledge of depth psychology and the importance of infantile experiences, little if any attention was paid to nipple holes. Confronted with an already overwhelming amount of detail in the proper rearing of offspring, it seems improper to add yet another detail. But is it really a detail?

Psychiatrists tell us that the infant's first relationship is an oral one. His first relatedness with the outside world then is sucking. What then if the nipple hole is too small and sucking should be hard? Or suppose that the milk comes out too easily. Surely the view of life of the infant confronted with a narrow nipple hole would be the envisionment of constant struggle, whereas nipples with excessively large holes may produce the easy-come, easy-go type of personality. Nipple holes that frequently clog may even be disastrous.

Let us imagine the following sad case. Edgar Wetzelgrid, in his autobiography *A Lifer Reminisces,* reveals that while doing three years in solitary, he was able to recall early infantile rages prompted by a clogged nipple hole. These rages followed him through life. One day after having consumed a fifth of whiskey, Edgar was attempting to remove the cork on a second fifth with his teeth and could not. In a blind fury, undoubtedly brought on by a reawakening of earlier emotional reactions to clogged nipples, Edgar slew his wife and her lover, who were taunting him at the time.

Realistically, a nipple hole that is too small may cause an infant to swallow air in his efforts to get formula. This in turn may cause him to spit up. It is quite common.

Nipples that have been frequently boiled get floppy around the opening very often, and the opening may have to be enlarged to get the milk out. A hatpin or needle, held over a match until the metal glows, can be used to enlarge the nipple hole quite satisfactorily. By the way, I do not think it is necessary to boil nipples if you have washed them thoroughly. That ought to eliminate the floppy nipple problem.

A nipple hole that is too large may cause the infant to take the formula quickly and consequently cause him to spit up.

A properly adjusted nipple hole should allow the milk to come from the bottle when it is turned over first in a steady stream, and then drop by drop.

WHENY WHEENY WINKY

At first glance this heading may seem to be a misrendered version of Caesar's report of his success in Gaul. Actually it is the phonetic duplication of a Chinese mother's question to a New York clinic doctor as to the best time to wean her son Win Ky. It is interesting that the question should be asked in the first place. It indicates that the cultural determinants which usually dictate when a mother should wean her infant are no longer present.

A Sioux mother in the recent past would not have weaned her infant until "three summers had gone by." The Sioux squaw not only did not wean her children until they were three years of age, but she was also in the habit of letting any passing child nurse from her if he wanted to. Lest one conclude that this practice made the little Sioux orally dependent and "Mama's babies," let me remind you that they were renowned for their fierceness as warriors.

A great deal of the problem as to when and how to wean your baby stems from Freudian theory. If infants go through an oral phase which is highly important in their character formation, then it follows that the time and manner in which this phase is ended could be extremely important. The trouble is that no one seems to know, or at least to agree, when is the best time. What is Mother to do?

On the one hand, there are doctors who feel that weaning either from the bottle or the breast should not be done before a year. They feel that, at this age, the baby's oral stage will be just about coming to an end. If he is deprived of his sucking before that time, he will have locked in his unconscious an unrequited passion for oral pleasure which will later affect his character. He may become garrulous, dependent, or an inveterate smoker. He is orally fixed, or, worse yet, he may need a fix.

On the other hand there are doctors who feel that the nipple can become an addiction. They feel that infants should be weaned as early as possible. One pediatrician has been encouraging mothers for many years to cup-feed their three-month-olds. The bewildered mother is liable to be offered a variety of opinions, depending, of course, on whom she asks. What can she do? Well, here are the straight facts.

There is no evidence whatsoever that the timing of weaning has any effect on personality. As a matter of fact, a retrospective study done on the children who had been weaned to the cup at three months of age showed no character traits peculiar to this group as opposed to a group of random children. So let us not worry about long term effects on character.

It has been shown that the earlier you wean, the easier it is in terms of not upsetting the child. I am talking about immediate upset, not long range upset. However, the immediate upset can be made worse by hesitancy on the mother's part. My own prejudice, notice I said prejudice, is to let the infant suck for at least six months to give the jaw some exercise. Most mothers in this country terminate breast-feeding at about six months when the infant gets teeth. You softies you.

After six months you can wean from the breast or bottle at any time. If you find that your baby resists weaning, you may wait until he is past two years of age, when studies indicate that resistance to weaning declines.

You are saying to yourself, "This guy has not helped much." I am not telling you when to wean the baby; I am giving you a choice. I am giving the baby a choice too. If he resists too much, wait; he'll probably be more willing later.

Paradoxically, and there is a truth to be learned in every paradox, the fact that there is not any right time should make you less hesitant. If you are still having trouble making up your mind, you may ask doctors on the one hand, or maybe doctors on the other hand. Listen, you wanted a family, didn't you?

WHEN, OH WHEN, SHOULD A BABY GET SOLID FOODS?

Probably no baby needs solid food before he is three or four months of age. The United States is probably the only country in the world that introduces solid foods earlier than that. The kinsmen of Anita Ekberg are ample proof that it is not necessary. No one suffers from later introduction of solids.

I am often asked when it is best to start giving the baby carrots, or when he can have pears. Frankly, there is no logical answer. Most doctors simply adopt an arbitrary schedule. It is important not to take it too seriously.

How much food should you give? Of course there are no exact amounts to feed an infant, anymore than there is an exact adult portion. Usually about one-third to one-half a jar is enough, but some babies can eat an entire jar and should be allowed to have it. Always offer some milk or formula first. Milk or formula is the most important food source for the infant.

Following is a suggested schedule for the introduction of various foods into your child's diet:

SSAS—The Simplified Suggested Arbitrary Schedule

1. From birth, any one of the three following daily:
   a. Mother's milk plus 0.3 cc of any standard vitamin preparation containing ADC.
   b. Any proprietary preparation up to 40 ounces per day—do not add vitamins (see page 41 to prepare one bottle at a time).
   c. Or formula as previously described made of: 13 ounces of evaporated milk (one can); 17 ounces of water; 2 tablespoons of table sugar or 2 tablespoons of light Karo syrup (see page 40 to prepare one bottle at a time) and 0.3 cc of any standard vitamin preparation containing ADC.
2. At two to three months add cereal.
3. At three months add orange juice or any other juice to which vitamin C has been added.
4. At three to four months add fruit.
5. At four months add vegetables.
6. At four to five months add egg yolks and meat.

Remember, no single food is important. For example, fruits and vegetables are interchangeable. Egg yolk is not important or necessary; meats are not necessary. I have been taking care of a family of strict vegetarians for many years, and they eat no animal products; that includes egg, milk, and meat. They are doing fine on carrot juice, beans, nuts, and fruit. I do not say they are healthier than any of my other patients, but they are certainly not less so.

How to Help the Vitamin Manufacturers Sell Vitamins

The vitamin intake in the United States is a scandal. When I last looked, it was a business with sales of over 300 million dollars, most of it completely unnecessary. More infants in the United States suffer from too many vitamins (hypervitaminosis), than from too little. In fact an infant receiving the equivalent of one pint of fortified milk per day, two ounces of orange juice, or some other juice containing vitamin C, requires no vitamin supplement. I have been advocating this procedure for ten years, and have never seen an infant develop anything resembling vitamin deficiency.

I hope that I have made some logical simplicity out of the whole mass of confusing information about infant feeding. And now let's feed the older children.

HOW TO UNBALANCE YOUR CHILD WITH A BALANCED DIET

I have no doubt that the following scene has been played many times in doctor's offices over the length and breadth of this overfed land of ours.

Cowering guiltily on a corner of the examining table is a rosy cheeked, round little six-year-old girl. The doctor is standing in midposition, between the child and her mother, as a sort of referee; and in the far corner, not even waiting for the bell to ring, is mother coming out fighting. "Doctor," she says, "she won't eat a thing. No matter what I put down in front of her, she won't eat. I don't understand it. She won't eat FOR me." "Well," the doctor usually says, trying somehow to divert the attacker, "tell me, for example, what she ate yesterday." This will stop her cold in her tracks because she has to remember something specifically. "Well," says the mother, somewhat uncertainly, "for breakfast, she had orange juice, cereal, and an egg and some milk, yes, but she did not even touch her cereal." "For lunch," the doctor prompts. "Well, she ate lunch in school. I think the menu said spaghetti. She could eat spaghetti until it comes out of her ears. I gave her money for ice cream. I guess she had that too." "How was supper?" I ask. "Let's see, for supper we had meatloaf and potato and salad." "Did she eat. . . ?" "Yes," she replies somewhat begrudgingly.

When I inquire politely as to just what is wrong with this diet, the mother arches her back, takes on a certain venomous facial expression, and says triumphantly, "But she won't eat lamb chops." For some reason or other there is a kind of love affair between the American mother and the lamb chop. I have the feeling that in an affluent society, if something is expensive, it is judged to be good. Lamb chops are expensive; therefore they must be good. When I tell a mother that there is no aristocracy in meats, that one meat equals the other, she will then murmur in retreat something about a "balanced diet."

Harping on the balanced diet is one way of unbalancing

your child. The concept has caused more mother-child dissonance than any other factor with the possible exception of rock 'n' roll. The American child in particular has such a wide choice of foods on which he may thrive that, realistically, there should be no problem. Instead, paradoxically, he suffers from abundance. Since the society can produce, he has to eat.

The Child Who Eats Small Quantities

Not long ago I was called to aid a four-year-old defendant whose mother was accusing him of being too thin. "Look at him," she was saying, "he is so thin his ribs are sticking out." The defendant was small, slender, vigorous, and active. The defendant's mother, was small, slender, vigorous, and active. When I inquired about his father, I was told that he was on the lean side until he got married. "I guess you can see my husband likes the willowy type," she said further. "He must, or he never would have gone for me."

Bamboo would have been the arboreal simile I would have chosen, but no matter.

I pointed out the genetic background, the hereditary stuff, from which her son was formed.

> *Thou slender, of thy mother's lightly laden womb,*
> *The little issue of thy father's loin,*
> *Thou thing of nature . . .*

To paraphrase Shakespeare's *Richard II.*

Her child's genetic destiny was to be small and slender. The small child requires small amounts of food. Small feedings don't make the small child.

A chihuahua could never be a boxer, no matter what its mother insisted he eat.

THE CHINESE MENU PLAN: HOW TO CURE ALL FEEDING PROBLEMS

No matter what type of feeding problem we are dealing with, the Chinese menu plan offers the possibility of a high degree of success. Mother has on hand some simply prepared foods, which we will list under A, B, or C.

For example:

A	B	C
Milk	Egg	Cereals (hot or
Soup	Salad	cold)
Frankfurters	Tomato juice	Cheese
Orange juice	Hamburger	Liverwurst
Carrots	Corn	Bacon
Peas		Spaghetti

You may decide for yourself what you want to place under A, B, or C.

A child may select either one from A and B, or one from A and C, or one from B and C, or two from A, two from B, or two from C, or none from either A, B, or C.

Even if he does not eat anything, at least he will learn the new math concept of sets.

If after fifteen minutes he has not touched his plate, you should remove it and state firmly that someone else is waiting for the table.

Very often a child eating on the Chinese menu plan will say about one hour later, "I don't know, that stuff doesn't really fill you up," and he will request more food.

A mother who feels somewhat insecure about this may offer fortune cookies, in which the little message reads: "Confucius says all children should eat."

The point of the matter is that a healthy child will regulate his own diet quite well. No child will starve to death if he is left alone.

A child receiving a pint of milk per day or a serving of meat two or three times a week, fruit or vegetables several times each week, is having an adequate diet as regards the basic foodstuffs. He will adjust his caloric requirements himself. As I have said before, daily consumption of one pint of whole milk and two ounces of orange juice, or some other vitamin C containing juice, will satisfy his vitamin requirements so that supplements are not necessary.

There is some evidence, I might add, that excessive intake of vitamin A or D will decrease the child's appetite. LET US ALL RELAX.

HOW TO BABYPROOF
YOUR HOME

When we get done thinking about the possibilities for accidents in the ordinary environment, you'll probably be sorry you had kids in the first place. But here they are, and here we are, so let's get going.

I am indebted to the New York State Department of Health, which is in turn indebted to the San Jose City Health Department, San Jose, California, for its safety leaflets, which supply much of the information for this chapter.

I shall list the safety precautions you need undertake according to age groups, noting fairly that it gets worse as the children get older. After seeing my list you may decide to take up with the Sahara bedouins, among whom the only risks are camel falls and the loss of personal daintiness.

BIRTH TO SIX MONTHS

You haven't got enough to worry about, what with making formulas and losing sleep. Now I'm going to bother you with accidents yet.

Bathing

Test the temperature of the water before putting the baby in it. Keep baby away from faucets. I can remember one tragic accident in which a baby toppled off a wash counter into the wash basin, striking and turning on the hot water faucet as he fell. He was severely scalded.

Remember, don't apply vaseline or baby lotion *before* you put the baby in the tub. This will make him waterproof and slippery. See the chapter on giving the baby a bath.

Falling

Never leave the baby on a high place unprotected. Quick as a flash, when you least expect it, he can fall over. Even if he doesn't hurt himself much, you'll be upset; and when your husband hears about it, watch out!

Feeding

Never prop a bottle. An infant can choke on it since he has no way of stopping the flow.

Swallowing

Don't leave any small objects near the infant that he might accidentally grasp and put in his mouth.

Smothering

Infants under one year of age don't need pillows and shouldn't have them. (Don't smother him psychologically either.)

Well, if this scares you, wait until we get to the one year old!

SIX MONTHS TO ONE YEAR

Let us assume that you survived the first six months. In the second six months the infant is motorized. By the end of the year, he will probably have the mobility and the gentility of a Sherman tank. You mothers who worry about your year-old infant not walking yet don't know what you are asking for. To compound the problem, the formerly placid creature who was content to lie on his back and coo has been converted into a behemoth who will put anything into his mouth that does not move; and I have seen exceptions to that rule, but delicacy prevents me from being specific.

Keeping Potential Poisons Out of Reach

Make sure that medications, particularly flavored aspirin, pleasant tasting and even not so pleasant tasting medications are kept out of reach. Liquids such as kerosene, gasoline, paint thinners, ammonia and other household cleansers, spot removers, and rug cleaners are particularly dangerous also.

Keeping Breakage to a Minimum

For your own piece of mind, I would keep table tops free of ash trays and cups and saucers, particularly if they are not open stock. It goes without saying that smaller objects should be kept out of reach, although it is surprising what a small child can swallow and pass with safety (see the section on the mouth in the chapter "One Thousand and One Ways Parents Get Gray").

Appliances

When I consider the possibilities of accidents in the American home, chock full of gadgets supposed to make life easier, I am not sure that the industrial revolution has really improved our way of life. The mother in Uganda may have an occasional bad-tempered lion to worry about, but that is as nothing compared to the booby traps in the average American home.

Electrical cords seem particularly to attract crawlers and should, in so far as possible, be kept out of reach. Children always seem to be wanting to put their fingers in holes. Jean-Paul Sartre regards this desire on the part of human beings to fill holes as an ontological, metaphysical problem. Parents who are interested in this problem can find the subject exhaustively covered in Sartre's book *Being and Nothingness*. Perhaps you had better wait until the kiddies are grown before you tackle it. In the meantime, I assure you that as a physician I can bear out his metaphysician's assumption that children like to put their fingers in holes. Let us get back to the problem at hand. There are now inexpensive devices on the market that you can place into unused electrical outlets; they will prevent the child from putting his fingers inside.

Kitchens

It is best to teach children right off that the kitchen is off limits. I was unable to do this with my own son, who was fascinated by the knobs on the stove. It almost drove my wife mad until we hit on the idea of removing the knobs when the stove was not in use.

As you probably will not be able to keep the children out of the kitchen, remember to keep poisonous substances well out of reach. You may find it useful to set up a special play area for the child in the kitchen. If you have the space, give him a low drawer or shelf to keep old pots and pans or plastic containers on, and if you are lucky he may play contentedly, and safely, with them all the time you are working in the kitchen.

ONE TO TWO YEARS

The child of one to two years has been called, somewhat euphemistically, a toddler. These toddlers are now full-fledged tanks, roaming and destroying as they go. Unfortunately, they can do damage to themselves in the following ways.

Falling

I would say that one good fall a month is about par for the course for the average "toddler." To cut down on this rate, I would suggest you install inexpensive safety gates at the tops of stairways. A good safety gate is one that an adult can unlock, but a young child can't. Falling out of automobiles is surprisingly common. Safety locks are available. I have always preferred two-door sedans, with the children in the back. It may be a little difficult for your mother-in-law to get into the back seat. That is a disadvantage? You should, of course, have seat belts for the entire family.

Drowning

It is a law in my part of the country that all pools and ponds be amply guarded from the child who might accidentally wander in. Children often do not have any idea of water depth or any innate fear of water. If you have a pool, it is a good idea to install an electric pool alarm which will go off whenever anything much heavier than a leaf falls in the water.

And, of course, never let a small child play unsupervised in a swimming pool, a wading pool, or even a bathtub.

I need not add that all of the precautions applicable during the first year of life are even more important during the second year. The price of parenthood is constant vigilance. All the precautions that I have mentioned should be kept in force until the children have reached the age of reason. I mean, of course, when they are capable of understanding the dangers implicit in a given object or situation.

A SAFETY CHECK LIST

A simple procedure for avoiding unnecessary anxiety about potential accidents is to make your own alert safety check of your home and immediate environment. Take your husband for an indoor walk, through every room, looking for objects or situations which might present a hazard for your toddler—and do something to correct it. Then do the same thing out-of-doors. Recheck periodically as a precaution.

Indoors

STAIRCASES: Do they have safety gates where needed?

WINDOWS: Do you open second floor (and higher) windows from the top only? Have you thought of buying window guards to keep children from falling through either open or closed upper story windows (children have been known to climb up on window sills and fall through the panes of closed windows)? Do you keep pieces of furniture on which a child can climb away from under windows?

ELECTRICITY: Can small children get at your electrical cords or trip over them? Do you have safety plugs in unused electrical outlets?

TABLE TOPS: Do you keep them free of breakable objects or dangerous objects that a child might swallow? Do you keep low tables with sharp corners out of the center of the room where small children might fall against them? Do you keep lighters and matches out of reach?

RUGS: Are your rugs securely anchored so that your child will not slip on them when running?

SHELVES AND BOOKCASES: Are they well anchored so they can't fall over on a child (remember, children love to climb bookcases)?

KITCHEN: Do you store all knives, forks, and other sharp implements out of reach of small children? Do you remember to place sharp implements while in use in the center of the table or counter where they cannot fall off on a child, or where the child cannot reach them when you are not looking? Do you remember when cooking always to turn the handles of pots away from the outside of the stove so that a child cannot grab them and you will not knock them off accidentally? Do you remember to keep *all* poisonous cleaning supplies locked away out of reach of children (a cupboard is not out of reach if the child can open the door by himself)? Do you remember *never* to put anything poisonous into an empty soft drink bottle (to a child, if it's in a soda bottle, it must be soda)? Are all matches out of reach of children? Are plastic bags out of reach of children?

BATHROOMS: Do you remember to close all medicine and cosmetic containers tightly and keep them out of children's reach? Locking medicine cabinets are highly recommended—and not just for medicines (it may be funny if 2-year-old Mary smears your lipstick all over her face and hair, but what if she decides to drink your nail polish?).

CLOSETS: Are you careful to arrange their contents so that things don't fall out of the closets when you open the door? Are all objects on high closet shelves placed securely so they won't fall on anyone's head? Do you destroy immediately the plastic bags that cover your clothes when they are brought home from the cleaners? Are you certain that there are no mothballs loose on closet floors or shelves (they are poisonous and children have been known to mistake them for candy)?

Outdoors

Are outdoor toys in safe shape, e.g. chains holding swings not rusted through or ropes holding tires frayed, bolts holding seesaws firmly in place, etc?

Do you have sharp metal guards around your flower garden that a child could cut himself on if he fell on them?

Do you have rusty or sharp pieces of machinery sitting around that a child could hurt himself on?

Are wells securely covered?

Are drain openings securely covered—so that a child can't lift the cover?

If you have a swimming pool, is it securely fenced in and kept locked when there is not an adult around to supervise?

Have you removed the door of an old refrigerator or freezer you may have stored in your garage?

Are there any boards with nails lying around in the yard?

Are gardening tools put away when not in use so that children will not fall over or on them?

SELECTING A
BABY-SITTER

Two articles in *The New York Times* put the selection of a baby-sitter on a more scientific basis.

The first article, on July 11, 1965, dealt with Allen Ginsberg, the poet. It likened his appearance to that of a Hasidic rabbi and mentioned his work in the promotion of the general use of marijuana.

The second article appeared on the first page of the Sunday *Times* of July 17, 1965. It dealt with a forthcoming book on sex crimes written by members of the Kinsey Foundation. I noted these pertinent facts:

First, sex crimes against children were less likely to be committed by strangers.

Second, drug users were less likely to commit these crimes.

Third, the incidence of commission of sex crimes was extremely low, if existent at all, among Jews.

The best baby-sitter should be the one your children would be safest with. Therefore, if you go by the statistics, a stranger who is a marijuana-smoking Jew would be best. If he is not a friend of yours, I suggest you call Allen Ginsberg.

Suppose you are not so fortunate as to have a baby-sitter with the above qualifications available. What can the conscientious parent do about baby-sitters?

Obviously, try to get someone you know, preferably a female. I am always a little wary about having an adolescent male baby-sit for a seven-year-old girl, no matter how nice he seems. Baby-sitting is kind of a woman's job anyway. If you do not know the sitter personally, try, of course, to get references. In a small town this is no problem.

Tell her clearly what she is expected to do in terms of feeding, bathing, and preparing children for bed. Do not overwhelm her. If it is someone mature, you may offend her by giving her too many directions.

Leave the telephone number where you can be reached in an emergency.

Leave the phone number of a neighbor with a car whom she can call on in case emergency transportation is necessary.

Above all, relax, have a good time, do not worry. I dare you! After all, accidents can happen whether or not you are at home, and you will be better parents for getting out once in a while.

FOR CRYING OUT LOUD, WHAT IS COLIC?

A harried mother of a two-month-old screaming child once asked me desperately, "For crying out loud, what is colic?"

"Colic is the name for crying out loud," I replied.

The causes of colic, both real and imaginary, are many, but the common factor is a crying infant who usually draws his legs up and acts as if he had abdominal pain. Colic is a symptom whose cause may or may not be detectable.

Some years ago an old pediatrician said to me, "It's the mothers of colicky infants who need the treatment." Years have taught me the error of this type of thinking.

In most instances it is not the mother who makes the baby cry. Rather, it is the other way round. "Doctor, I am sorry to break down in front of you this way, but it has got the best of me," are words I have heard frequently. Sure Mother is nervous and upset, but who would not be after being cooped up all day with a crying infant? A recent study of the mothers of colicky infants failed to reveal any factors in their emotion or behavior that might have been responsible for the colic in the infant. O.K., if it is not the mother, then what is it?

THE POSSIBLE CAUSES OF COLIC

Hunger

Colicky babies are rarely hungry. I have not found, therefore, strengthening the formula or adding solids to be helpful. On the contrary, colicky babies are usually well-fed, plump, and vigorous.

The danger, if any, is overfeeding.

Cow's Milk Allergy

Allergy is particularly likely to be the cause of colic if there is a family history of eczema, hay fever, asthma, or other allergic disorders. Milk allergy, though not common, is also not as rare as one might imagine. This allergy is a sensitivity to one of the two proteins in milk: either to the lactalbumin or the casein. If the lactalbumin is the cause, a switch from whole milk to an evaporated milk formula will eliminate that problem. Lactalbumin in evaporated milk has been denatured and consequently does not cause allergy. If the colic is caused by sensitivity to casein, however, a change from cow's milk is necessary. There are a wide variety of formulas to choose from. There are several soybean preparations available, and they are most economical. The other preparations one can try are made up of partially-digested animal protein, meat base, lamb base, or goat's milk. The point is to try some preparation that does not contain cow's milk protein. The new formula may produce a dramatic change for the better, but even if it doesn't, it should be tried for at least a week.

Reactions to Specific Sugars

Recently it has been discovered that some infants lack a particular enzyme necessary to digest a particular sugar. For example, an infant might be deficient in or lack sucrase, the enzyme for sucrose, common table sugar, or lactase, the enzyme for lactose, the milk sugar. Most of these infants, in addition to being irritable, vomit, have loose stools, and lose weight. My guess is that mild forms of this sugar intolerance exist, and can be the cause of colic. Sometimes a change to a formula with a different sugar helps these colicky infants greatly. In any event, changing the sugar in the formula might be worth a try.

The Little Belly Acher

I'll have to admit that despite our best efforts at changing formulas, there are a substantial number of babies whom nothing seems to please. They are always unhappy. They don't seem to know what they want. They are always "belly aching." These babies are the really tough ones. They can drive you out of your mind. There is one compensation. They usually get well by three months of age. In the meantime there are various things you can try. Pacifiers are helpful for some. Stretching the rectal sphincter is helpful for others. Correcting constipation may be helpful. Your doctor, of course, can do this.

Anti-spasmodic drops may be used. I have had some good results with whisky—any brand will do. Add twenty drops to one ounce of water and one-half teaspoon of sugar.

We don't know why these babies behave this way, but I think we have at least learned not to blame the mother always.

HURTS YOU?

PACIFIERS, OR, A SUCKER IS BORN EVERY MINUTE

There is something about pacifiers that upsets parents, particularly fathers. I have a vivid memory of a father of a patient of mine who was chomping and chewing on an unlit cigar, saying to me, "If there is one thing I cannot stand, it's a pacifier." When I pointed out his own oral activities, the best he could reply was, "Well that is different." He did not specify what "that" was or even how it differed. The best answer to this father and others in the antipacifier wing of this country was supplied by a precocious pacifier-user aged three. He was sitting quietly in a chair, sucking on his pacifier in a roomful of his parents' friends. A lady who caught sight of him launched into a strong attack against pacifiers. She complained that they were a bad habit, they were "dirty," and she could not see how parents could let their child have one. The child listened for a while, turned toward the speaker, and said, "Hurts you?"

The pacifier in this country has had its ups and downs. Anyone who has had a three-month-old who keeps dropping his pacifier out of his mouth and crying through the night will know what I mean. I also mean this in a historical sense. In the 1920's and thirties it was unpopular. Somehow in my mind I tie this up with Prohibition. Sometime in the 1940's, after the repeal of the eighteenth amendment, it became more popular. The scientific impetus for this came from Dr. David Levy's work on dogs. Puppies deprived very early of nursing showed later evidence of this deprivation by engaging in a great deal of extra-nutritional sucking. He reasoned that there was a certain sucking need, which if not gratified early in life would leave a hangover in the form of a desire to suck. In the human, this might manifest itself in the form of thumb-sucking or possibly smoking. Pediatricians, therefore, were quick to suggest the pacifier as a way of preventing thumb-sucking or oral deprivation. Presumably, if you were Freudian enough in your outlook, this could have characterological implications. All this from a little rubber plug.

Actually, the matter is not nearly so serious. Some children like to suck more than others. They are happier with a pacifier. What is wrong with a little happiness? The trouble is that pacifiers become an addiction. The child uses it to comfort himself, the experience gets reinforced, and you cannot get the darn thing away. I have found that it is best to take it away at around one year. It does not affect the jaw or teeth permanently at that time. By the way, there are pacifiers so constructed that they, even if sucked into adulthood—that is a frightening thought!—will never cause overbite. Anyway, you can take the pacifier away at one year of age—abruptly. Get every last one out of the house though, and settle down for three days of unhappiness. What is wrong with a little unhappiness? Then it is all over. By the way, if you allow your child to have a pacifier, be prepared for criticism.

My own son still had his pacifier at the age of three. I guess I did not like a little unhappiness. We were walking in the local shopping center. An acquaintance saw us and without bothering to say hello, she stated in a rather loud voice, "A pediatrician's child with a pacifier!" "Well," I replied, "he does not know I am a pediatrician."

One word of warning: pacifiers that are sweetened with honey or sugar water, if used repeatedly, may cause destruction of the tooth enamel and cavities.

DON'T THROW OUT THE BABY
WITH THE BATH WATER

A mother performs three functions for a baby. She feeds him, she keeps him clean, and she loves him. You can teach a mother to feed a baby. You can teach her to keep a baby clean. She will love a baby if she is free from apprehension. Anxiety inhibits loving. Anxiety makes the mother feel closed in, isolated, and unable to give to the baby, which is loving. I know this sounds preachy, and you may ask, what does this have to do with giving a baby a bath. Well, the point is that one can stir up so much apprehension about bathing a baby that it becomes a torture.

Let us start with the essentials. You bathe a baby to keep him clean. In performing this elementary task, you try to do it as simply as possible, without doing the baby any harm. The water is kept reasonably warm, so as to be comfortable for the baby. This does not mean that cold water will hurt a baby or "chill" him or give him a cold. Generations of Eskimo mothers have undressed their babies in sub-freezing temperature without adverse effect. The O'Flaherty film *Nanook of the North* shows an Eskimo mother holding a nude infant in her arms. Your infant and the Eskimo infant (I am assuming you are not an Eskimo) have the same ability to withstand cold. So you can see that the exact temperature is not too important.

In the beginning you can sponge-bathe the baby. Let us say for the first week. Until you get used to each other. After this you can bathe the baby in a tub, sink, bath, or bucket, or any other suitable receptacle. Hold him in any way you feel secure. Just remember that a soapy baby is a slippery baby. You do not want to lose him in the bath water. The best way to learn is to have somebody with a good safety record in baby baths show you.

Any plain white soap will do. There is no virtue in one soap over another.

I assume that when the baby bath is over you want to dry him with a towel. If you need any special direction about that, you are in trouble.

Powdering babies is not essential. If you want to powder the baby under the arms and under the diapers, any old talc will do. I prefer talc to cornstarch because cornstarch is a carbohydrate and bacteria grow in it. It can occasionally be a source of skin infection.

A baby lotion has no special virtue. Its purpose is to shine up the baby for company, but other than that there is no special need for it. Some lotions give a higher gloss than others. Even the baby who at birth seems to have dry skin will spontaneously develop normal skin without the application of lotion.

Some simple vaseline applied to the diaper area at the first sight of redness is an excellent way to prevent diaper rash. The most important way to prevent diaper rash, however, is not with lotion or creams. Diaper rash is due to the release of ammonia from the urine by the action of certain bacteria. If these bacteria are not destroyed in the diapers, they will release ammonia which irritates the infant's skin and causes diaper rash. One teaspoonful of Borax added to a gallon of water and used to soak diapers before washing will prevent diaper rash. If you use a diaper service this is not necessary.

I know there has been a lot of confusing nonsense concerning bath soaps and lotions. All the intelligent mother needs is a cool head, a warm bath, a plain white soap, any talc, and some vaseline, and she is in business. Be certain to keep these in proper order. Greasing your infant with vaseline before putting him in the bath tub, will make him a water-repellent, slippery infant.

Just remember: soap and water first.

BABY, IT'S COLD OUTSIDE

Thou nurse in swaddling bands the babe enfold
And carefully defend its limbs from the cold.
If winter, by the chimney place the chair.
If summer, then admit the cooling air.

This old English quatrain both reflects the ancient concern with environmental temperatures and expresses our unchanged modern attitude.

The modern baby book will give the mother some guidelines as to when to take the baby out and how to dress him. They usually express this as a relationship between weight of the baby and the outside temperature. The following is a more specific guide.

The Temperature Weight Index

The temperature weight index is a scientific method for determining whether baby should go out or not. The index is arrived at by multiplying the weight in pounds by the temperature in Fahrenheit. Any attempts to do this with kilograms may prove, if not disastrous, at least confusing.

Let us say the baby weighs seven pounds, and the temperature is 72, the index will be 504. If the index is greater than 500, baby may go out. In temperate climates, as the weight approaches temperature, your child can increasingly make his own decisions. Thus if the temperature is sixty and his weight is sixty, his T. W. I. is 3600, way beyond the index of consent. So if he says, "Ma, I am going out," that is O.K.

The full-term infant, that is the infant that has been carried for nine months, with a weight of over five and one-half pounds, has various ways to cope with fluctuations of the temperature in the environment. It works as follows. The human infant, as is the adult, is a warm-blood animal. I mean by this that he tries to keep his body temperature at a constant level. Whether it is very cold or very hot, the body temperature remains at about 98.6° F. At this temperature, the infant or adult functions best. He maintains this temperature by various means. If the environmental temperature rises, the metabolism may fall. If it is cold, the metabolism rises. In addition, there is a temperature control center in the brain. Adrenal hormones also respond to changes in the external temperature.

Another means of temperature control is brown fat, which is present in certain areas of the infant's body. It serves as insulation and an energy source to keep temperature constant.

The question is, what are the limits of tolerance of these mechanisms in keeping the temperature constant? They are really not completely known. It is evident, however, that the full-term infant can withstand the same fluctuations in temperature that the average adult can, *regardless of his specific weight*. You see, you do not need a scale and a thermometer to determine whether you can go out.

Curiously the danger in going out is not the temperature. The main danger is exposure to people with infections. As I have mentioned at other times—it bears repeating—contrary to popular belief, the newborn infant does not have good immunity to all infections. He may be particularly susceptible to many types of infection, particularly respiratory infections. Therefore, when you decide to go out of doors, be more careful of whom you meet than what the temperature is. I advise no particular restrictions based on weight. I do not think I would take the baby out in weather that either you or he would find uncomfortable. I do not see any particular virtue in "fresh air." If you want to go out, please do so. Stay out as long as you wish. Dress for comfort. Show off your baby. Have a good time.

TOILET-TRAINING,
THE MODERN MOVEMENT

Many parents approach toilet-training with fear and trembling; many children wind up with fear and trembling. Pediatricians and psychiatrists have varied in their advice as to how to toilet-train infants.

In general, I find, there are two group of parents that one contends with.

There are those parents who are conversant with Freudian theory. They feel that the toilet-training period is fraught with psychological dangers. They believe that the child who, as a result of early toilet-training, tries to hold back his stool, will be a stingy, stubborn, and suspicious person. In essence they believe that the personality of the child and the stool are molded in the same fashion. The constricted child has constricted stools. It is natural, therefore, that these parents are scared and tend to be permissive. It is not uncommon for children in these families not to be toilet-trained until they are three or four years old. The story is told of one infant prodigy who was invited to be a guest conductor of the New York Philharmonic. The offer was withdrawn when it was learned he was not toilet-trained.

The other group of parents are unaware of the psychological aspects of the problem. They want to get over "having a mess" as soon as possible. This group approaches toilet-training very early—some at under one year, and they will persist with unabated fury until the child is trained or an impasse is reached. There was one father I know of who threatened to rub his eighteen-month-old daughter's nose in her "spoor" if she would not stop messing because this method had worked with his dog.

Recently a well-known pediatrician suggested placing a potty seat in the middle of the living room and having the child practice-sit for a few minutes each day, to get him or her over any possible fear of the commode. The child starts by sitting fully clothed, and gradually, I suppose, is seduced into removing his pants. After months of this he is presumably reassured and gets the idea.

Other pediatricians have now suggested that toilet-training at about one year of age not only is not such a bad idea, but that the one-year-old be fully trained at this age. The various theories on toilet-training have been so confusing and anxiety-provoking that some parents have regressed and gone back to soiling themselves.

Let us treat toilet-training as a practical affair.

Among primitive people who have no toilet facilities and who are not concerned about cleanliness, toilet-training is not a problem. If we do not take seriously the relationship of the gastrointestinal tract to the development of the personality (which I don't), we are immediately freed from the awful consequences of our error. If you can train or catch your one-year-old—more power to you.

If you want to toilet-train at any age, do so. If, for whatever reason, toilet-training becomes a battle between you and the child and you become obsessed with the need to toilet-train, then it will have repercussions on the child. If you get angry with him, he will probably get angry with you. If parents consistently get angry with a child, he may later have the feeling that everyone is angry with him. This may be at the root of a personality problem later. Parents are sometimes less than candid about this.

A famous pediatrician, Dr. Bass, tells this story. He was consulted by the parents of a child with a stool problem. Dr. Bass felt that the parents had been aggravating the situation by constantly reminding the child that he ought to have a bowel movement. He discussed this with the parents, asked them to de-emphasize bowel movements, and asked them to return in several months.

On their return visit, Dr. Bass consulted with the parents prior to his examination. The parents assured him that they had never mentioned the subject to the boy, but nevertheless, the problem persisted. Then Dr. Bass went into the examining room to see the child. He said, "Good morning." The child replied, "Good morning, Dr. Bass. Did you have a bowel movement this morning?"

The Saga of the Sentimental Stool Holder.

In the course of a routine history taking of a two-year-old child, I happened to ask how toilet-training was going. "It was going fine," said the mother, "until a few weeks ago. It seems so silly, and I am almost embarrassed to tell you.

"A few weeks ago, Roger began noticing his stools. He had not paid any attention before, but now as they lay in the commode and were flushed away, he seemed in a strange way to be moved by this. On the very last day before our problem developed—it happened to be New Year's day—the radio was blaring sentimentally with Auld Lang Syne, and Roger waved bye-bye to his bowel movement. I was so touched that I became tearful. I guess it was the wrong attitude to take. Ever since he holds back and will not go for several days. When he does go, it hurts. I know it is silly Doctor, but I really do not think he wants to give up his stools."

Intrinsic in every problem are the designs for the solution. I suggested to the mother that she give the child large amounts of mineral oil, as much as three tablespoons and more if necessary, to make the parting less painful. I also suggested that at the time of his next bowel movement, she dress gaily, assume a hard-bitten attitude, and let him have his bowel-movement to the tune of "I'll be Glad When You're Dead You Rascal You."

Whatever the cause of stool holding, be it sentiment, stubbornness, cold toilet seats, sitting (some children have difficulty having a stool from a sitting position), mineral oil is an excellent aid.

As a matter of practical fact, if your milder efforts have not succeeded by two to two and one-half years of age, children usually will toilet-train themselves at that age by imitation. It is interesting to note that some children do not control their movements unless both their feet are on the ground; they, of course, do better on a low potty seat.

BOWEL MOVEMENTS ARE NOT WORTH FIGHTING OVER.

HOW I LEARNED TO STOP
WORRYING AND LOVE BEDTIME

THE THEORETICAL BEDTIME SITUATION

Naturally you want to keep bedtime as agreeable and as happy as possible. Going to bed, whether for a nap or the night, can be a delightful experience, even for the child, if you do not make it unpleasant. The question is how.

First of all, have an attitude of cheerful assuredness about it. Never mind that your car broke down, or the plumber did not keep his promise to come and fix the stopped up toilet and the whole house smells. Forget the back pains you have had ever since your seventh child was born. Have an air of cheerful certainty.

Naptime Is Fun Time

It is usually best to have a nap right after lunch. After lunch, simply say, in a breezy, cheerful, self-confident, firm but not harsh, assured but not domineering, soft but audible tone, "It is time to have our NAPPIE now." If you have done this properly, most children, not all children, will usually, not always, sometimes, go to bed without protesting. Of course, sometimes they may protest. It is too much to expect a two-year-old to be pleasant always. Even you will be out of sorts sometimes.

Beddy-bye Time

Beddy-bye time is a much more complicated situation. The children are excited about Dad's coming home. In

71

some families, children wait for Dad to come home before they have their dinner; in others, children are fed dinner before Father comes home. Remember, you have the right to make important decisions. You may find it convenient to feed your children before your husband arrives home. You need not feel guilty about this. Many parents tend to feel guilty about minor things. Psychologists have shown that these parents usually have had unhappy childhoods. They usually resent their parents and as a consequence have developed guilt feelings toward them. Their children in turn resent their guilt-ridden parents and develop their own guilt feelings. Yes, children, even tiny ones, can have great big guilt feelings.

Well, let us say that you have said to your baby in a cheerful, breezy, self-confident, assured but not domineering, soft but audible tone, "Jeffrey, it is beddy-bye time." Jeffrey replies, "Beddy-bye, my foot." At this point your instinct will be to reply in a definitely uncheerful, harsh, strident, loud, hysterical voice, "God damn it, will you get the hell to bed!"

You are thinking unconsciously, "I have had a terrible day. I wish these kids would go to bed. Jack said he would be on the six-ten train. I bet he stopped off for a drink at Grand Central Station. Gee, he *has* been drinking a lot lately. I wonder if I ought to take him to A A. They say that alcoholism starts off with social drinking. If you catch it early, there is a good chance it may be stopped. I will think about that later and try getting these kids off to bed."

Try to suppress, notice I said suppress, not repress, these feelings.

Some children are a little stubborn, and it may be necessary for you to repeat in a cheerful, breezy, self-confident, firm but not harsh, assured but not domineering, soft but audible voice, "It is beddy-bye time." Try to modulate your voice a little bit each time so that it may not be too monotonous. Some children will not respond if they are addressed in a monotonous tone. If, after this, he will not go to bed, you may have to drag him.

Naturally you expect your child to turn in when you want him to, but it is good for a child to feel that he can change his parents' mind once in a while. So you let him stay up a little longer on exceptional occasions, like . . .

the Day of the Power Failure. After all, we must not be too rigid.

SOME SERIOUS THOUGHTS ABOUT SLEEP PROBLEMS

I have myself spent many a sleepless night trying to figure out the best way to handle sleeping problems in children. I do not think this easy to handle, nor do I think that I or most parents are immune to them. It is generally agreed by pediatricians that there has been a rise in sleep problems as permissiveness has increased. The lesson to be learned from this equation is that we parents have to be firmer.

Many parents, for example, will run into an infant's room the moment he whimpers. They are terribly afraid that something might happen. The result of their insecurity is to establish an unfortunate behavior pattern in the child. The child awakens momentarily or has trouble falling asleep; he lets out a little cry and expects his mother or father to appear. Once he gets used to this, he will cry even harder if they do not appear. Once you are in this bind, it is difficult to get out. If this pattern has been established, it is worth letting the baby cry it out. The neighbors may not be able to sleep for a few nights, but eventually you will. After all, it is not your fault that builders are allowed to put up such thin walls.

Older children may make all sorts of excuses to get mother or father to come into the room after they have been put to bed. It is best to try to handle this firmly. It is all right for the child to be up as long as he stays in bed. It is unwise to yield to his demands for water or this or that just as an excuse to get attention. Of course, if he awakens with a nightmare, as many children between the ages of one and three do, he needs comforting. Most parents can feel when a child is genuinely frightened and needs them, and they can recognize, too, the child who is trying to manipulate them. In essence, what I am saying is that good sleeping patterns are habit formations. In a sense, the child must learn to sleep in some conformity with the needs of the household. Sometimes it is painful to learn something, but that is the way life is.

Some parents think that a child needs more sleep than
he actually does. We know that children's sleep needs vary
greatly. I have known infants who do well on nine hours'
sleep a day—I hope not yours—and others who are tired
and grumpy if they do not get fourteen hours a day. If
your child will not go to sleep at seven when you want
him to, you may find that he does not need that two-hour
afternoon nap. Once out of that habit, it won't be long before he will sleep ten hours straight through. In general, I
find that children up to two can take two naps a day.
From two until five I find that they need one.

There are some children who previously went to bed
without fussing who, usually at about nine months of age,
will suddenly start to scream and holler as soon as they
are put to bed. With such a child, you have to make com-
promises. Sometimes you will have to sit by the bedside
awhile, sometimes when older he will insist on a story
being read, or sometimes he will insist on going to bed
with a toy or doll. Most children have some kind of bedtime ritual. Honor it. If after a reasonable time, say about
half an hour, you have made no progress, insist on leav-
ing. He may cry and scream awhile but finally will go off
to sleep. On the other hand—there goes the other hand—
there are children who, despite your best efforts, will not
go to sleep, or if they do they will constantly reawaken.

If the firm approach mixed with a dose of compassion
is not successful, you may have to ask the doctor for medication. There is nothing wrong with doing this. Many parents when offered this help will state that they do not want
their child drugged or express fear that the child will become addicted. My answer is that these drugs are harmless
in proper doses and you will use them for only two weeks
or so until good sleeping patterns get established. I have
found that the best drug for this purpose is chloral hy-
drate. Some children are stimulated by barbiturates, such
as phenobarbital, so I usually do not recommend them.

THE ALTERNATE SIDE PARKING TECHNIQUE: HOW TO DECIDE WHAT IS THE BEST POSITION FOR YOUR BABY TO SLEEP IN

If you take a moment in your busy day for reflection, you will see that there are four possible positions that your baby can sleep in. He can sleep on his back, he can sleep on his abdomen (you may know it better as his "tummy"), or he can sleep on either the right side or the left side. I think that about covers it. Confronted with all these choices, how can you decide what is best to do? First, of course, we can simplify it by narrowing your choice down from four to three. As far as I know it makes no difference whether your child lies on his right or left side. I suppose that if placing the baby on his right side meant he would be facing the wall, you might decide to put him on the left side, unless you decided to put the head of the crib where the foot of the crib was, in which case you would not have to move the baby. Do you follow me so far?

Now there are two other variables in this fast-complicating situation. How does the baby want to sleep, and how do the experts want him to sleep? Some babies prefer to sleep on their backs and others prefer to sleep on their tummies. They seem to be neutral about sleeping on their sides. Cultural influences seem to be important. In the United States most babies sleep on their tummies while in England practically all infants sleep on their backs.

It has been suggested that the well-known British characteristic of always looking up in the face of disaster may have derived from this sleeping position. On the other hand the tummy position of the American infant, his face always facing a white sheet, may account for the American problem of *ennui* and its resolution by staring at television screens, even when they are blank.

As if all this did not present us with enough of a problem, let us consider the effect of back or stomach sleeping on leg malalignments. Mrs. Mabel Lum Fitzhugh, whose work is referred to in the *Family Book of Child Care* by Niles Newton, found that babies who slept either on their backs or their tummies had leg malalignments. She advocates putting the infant on alternate sides—on different occasions of course. For instance you might put him on his right side on Monday, Wednesday, and Friday. On his left side on Tuesday, Thursday, and Saturday. Sunday can be divided into right and left or you can use the alternate Sunday plan. You are to reverse all of this of course during leap year, or when oysters are not in season, or when the sun sets on the British Empire.

There are babies who insist on lying on one side or the other. This may result in some flattening of that side of the head. This head flattening corrects itself as the baby gets older, usually at around two years of age. Actually, the solution may be a simple one. Perhaps the baby merely wants to look out toward the light rather than toward the wall. If you put his head where his feet were, he will have to turn his head to the other side to see out. The flattening will be corrected.

Moral: Position is not everything in life. Put the baby in any position he is happy in. The only precaution I suggest is that if you place him on his abdomen, make sure he can lift his head, and that the mattress is firm.

HOW MANY TIMES
IS NORMAL?

Like many pediatricians I usually have a call-hour between the hours of 8 and 9 in the morning. I am usually prepared for anything, but I will admit to having been taken by surprise on hearing a mother, without salutation or introduction announce, "Susan is masturbating." Now, I do not mean that I was surprised that Susan was masturbating. In a sense it is her privilege, and in a way none of my business. "Is that normal?" Mother went on. Although I did not know which Susan she was talking about, the one who was three years old, or the fifteen-year-old, nor did I know whether she was doing it overtly or covertly, I muttered something about all children, including Susan, do it. "How many times is normal?" asked the Mother. I suppose if I had said fifteen times is normal for her weight and age, this mother would have either encouraged her to increase her activities by two or knock off a little earlier.

Another worried mother once asked me, "Isn't it true that the average two-year-old has temper tantrums, sleep problems, is stubborn and obstinate?" Seeking to reassure her I replied with that old bromide, "Yes, it is a stage that they all go through." It was a therapeutic misfire. "Doctor, I am worried. He does not have any problems he is supposed to have."

One of the problems of American parents is that they confuse average with normal. Obviously, if we say that the average baby walks at 14 months, it represents a statistic derived from the experience of let us say 100 or 1000 babies. A baby may walk at nine months or eighteen months and be normal, though decidedly not average.

77

HOW TO MAKE SURE YOUR CHILD IS NORMAL, OR HOW TO PUT THE TOT BEFORE THE COURSE

It is characteristic of our time that if enough people do something, at least 50.1 per cent, it will be accepted as normal.

I am already seeing evidences of the new preoccupation with statistical normalcy. During a routine examination of a nine-month-old infant, the mother reassured me—a reversal of our traditional roles—that her infant was developing completely normally. I asked her why she was so sure. "Well," she said, "I took a course in infant and child development. I know what is normal for a given age and I make my baby do it." This bit of reversal, of putting the tot before the course, so to speak, is one way that American mothers control their anxiety as to whether their children are normal or not.

It is important that parents realize that there are great variations in development. In general, an infant's development, particularly his motor development, is a fairly orderly procedure. It takes place in a cephalad to caudad direction, that is, from head to toe.

A newborn infant can move his head and raise it slightly. He also can move his eyes from side to side. I am often asked when can a baby see. Surprisingly, an infant can see from birth.

When my daughter was born, my wife asked me when the baby would be able to see. When I replied that she could already see, I was countered with skepticism. Being a pediatrician in no way makes me immune to wifely skepticism. I picked up a bright red rose from a bouquet sent my wife and held it in front of our daughter. She was not as skeptical as my wife. Although she was only an hour old, she definitely followed the rose. It is true that infants will only respond to a bright red object, and that they do not see clearly, but they do have vision. Clear vision, the ability, for example, to distinguish one face from other, probably develops around three months of age, when the macula, a special part of the retina of the eye, is completely developed.

After head movements, the infant learns to control his

neck movements. By three months of age an infant can raise his head completely when lying prone.

Proceeding downward, we come to the arms. An infant begins moving his arms in response to an object at about four months of age. He cannot reach for anything, but his arms will move in response to the sight of an object. At about this time you may see a child apparently looking at his fist and following with his head and eyes. He is experiencing eye-hand coordination.

In the next few months the infant learns to use his arms and hands in a skilled manner. By five months, he can usually reach for an object. By seven months he can transfer objects from hand to hand. By nine months he can grasp things well. He is beginning to use his thumb. The use of the thumb, from a philogenetic point of view, distinguishes man from the ape. It makes possible the manual ability of man to make tools and weapons. I do not mean to state that your infant can prepare an arsenal. You may have to wait until he is at least three for that. The trajectory from the bow and arrow to the atom bomb is a straight line with the thumb and the brain as the constants.

Development of the body is going on simultaneously with its appendages. At about five to seven months of age an infant can sit with support. If, for example, he is placed in a high chair firmly, he can be expected to sit comfortably. "But won't that hurt his back?" I can hear you ask. The answer is, NO. When an infant can sit comfortably with support, even if it is as young as four months, doing it will not hurt its back. (The fear of "hurting" the back probably stems from the time when rickets was common. In rickets, the bones are soft and distortions of the bones of the spine or legs could take place from early sitting or walking.) Somewhere between seven months and nine months, an infant can sit unsupported. He usually cannot get up to a sitting position by himself, but when placed there, can maintain it. All of this involves the development of the back muscles and nerves. It is not a question of strength only but of the ability, due to development of the proper nerves, to maintain muscular balance.

Below the back, the legs. The infant next learns to crawl. Curiously many infants learn to crawl backward. The majority of infants crawl forward at anywhere from ten to twelve months. Some young radicals skip crawling altogether and take off right away and walk. Walking is very variable. Some perfectly normal children do not walk until they are eighteen months old. The average age for walking in this country is fourteen months.

I started off by telling you the story of the mother who made her infant *follow* the norms of development. There is a fallacy to that type of thinking. An Indian story, I think, will make the point. There are two groups of Hopi Indians. There are those who mainly live in the towns and follow the standard American child-rearing customs. They allow the child to crawl or walk at will. In fact, if they are like the most of us, they encourage it.

The other group live on reservations and adhere to their old customs. They swaddle their young and carry them around papoose style until they are about one year of age. Now the shocker! The average age for walking is the same in both groups. It is about thirteen months. This illustrates rather strikingly that development in the normal infant takes place in an orderly predetermined head to foot manner, despite our efforts either to foster or thwart it. Now what do you think of parental influence!

You have probably noticed that I have concentrated on motor development. I started with this because it is much easier to grade motor development than the other aspects of development, social adaptation and language. I stressed that even in motor development, there are wide variations of the normal. Motor development is relatively uninfluenced by environmental factors. That is not the case for the other aspects of development. Let me outline briefly some of the average—notice I did not say normal —milestones.

Smiling: The earliest social response is smiling. It is an innate response that is reinforced by positive experience. An infant will smile automatically at a mask shown full face if the teeth are bared. This response usually takes place at about 6 weeks. Mothers will often report smiling at one or two weeks of age. What passes for smiling then is a grimace as wind passes.

Laughing aloud usually occurs at about four months of age.

Awareness of the Mother: Recently I received a frantic call from the mother of a two-week-old infant. She was convinced that he could not see her. Her evidence was that she could not get the child to follow her with his eyes. It turned out that he could see perfectly well, but that he did not fix his eyes on her. Many infants do not do this until they are three months of age.

Holding his own: A child will hold his own bottle or a teething biscuit when he is about six months old. Of course, there are great variations in this.

Feeding himself: The average child in our culture will be able to feed himself, albeit messily, at about fifteen months of age. Some depth psychologists feel that the child is deliberately messy because he enjoys it as an anal erotic experience. It is certainly true that children of about one year of age finger paint with creamed spinach, plaster the crevices in the table with liver, and would literally use pancake make-up. This behavior is a result of lack of coordination and an absence of learned esthetic behavior. Anyway, the thought that my child feeding himself was undergoing an anal erotic experience would make me lose my appetite.

It might be worthy to note here that children of fifteen months of age *like* to feed themselves. Parenthetically, their food needs are not so great. I have, I think, prevented many an incipient "feeding problem" by informing the mother of these facts. I have suggested that she place simple foods in front of the baby, surround his feeding table or high chair with old newspapers—or even current newspapers, the way things have been going lately—and let the baby go to it. He can learn his table manners later.

Toilet training is so variable that I do not think it has any relevance as a guide to development.

Language development: It is probably true that early development of language is the best indicator of high intelligence. But a parent should not assume the opposite. Late talkers may be extremely intelligent.

An infant will ordinarily coo at about two months. I hope it is not shocking if I note that the first syllables an infant utters are Da Da. He does this out of context, usually by nine months. At ten months he usually says Ma Ma, again out of context.

Single words usually develop at about a year, phrases later, and simple sentences by two. Again let me warn you that there are great variations in all of this. Speech is apparently a developmental phenomenon. The speech center is an area in the fore-brain, localized on the same side of the brain that controls handedness. A right-handed child has a left-sided speech center. Curiously, children who do not develop a dominant hand early do not develop expressive speech early, although their comprehension is good. I have had the experience many times of a child who could understand and follow out requests in two languages yet barely spoke either. One aside of importance: a child with delayed speech ought to have his hearing evaluated.

Let me caution you against taking any single developmental milestone seriously. The fact that a child walks a little late, or talks later than usual, need not be significant. An article entitled "The Backward Intelligent Child" by R. S. Illingworth in *Clinical Pediatrics*, October 1965, stresses this very point in his review of the biographies of famous men. Louis Pasteur was a slow learner. Einstein purportedly did not talk until three. Edison was a below average pupil. Illingworth fails, however, to mention Homer T. Bungle, who was slow in walking, slow in talking, an indifferent student, and despite this, never amounted to anything. Not every story has a happy ending.

WHY THE PSYCHOLOGICAL THEORIES ON BED-WETTING DON'T HOLD WATER

If you were a nineteenth-century parent of a bed-wetter you might have forced your child to eat the testicles of a rabbit, the hooves of a goat, or, if you were more esthetically inclined, the petals of a chrysanthemum. The modern parent is not asked to make his child swallow any of these remedies, but he has been asked to swallow some equally unpalatable psychological theories. Psychiatrists and psychologists have proffered a great many theories in regard to bed-wetting, or enuresis as it is known in the trade. Some have stated that it is a substitute for masturbation, in that a child experiences pleasure from the warm stream of urine. Even on a cold night? Others feel that it is a desire to return to a more infantile state, a psychological regression.

I would like to state flatly, that, in my experience, most bed-wetting is not psychologically caused. This is borne out in a recent British study of over 100 children. The findings were that bed-wetting simply got better as the child got older. The longer one waited, the more likely the symptoms were to disappear. EVEN IF NOTHING WERE DONE. In addition they were not able to demonstrate any evidence of neurotic traits in most of their patients. These British researches concluded that bed-wetting was a developmental disorder. Just as there are marked variations in walking and talking, there are children who develop bladder control late.

A recent pamphlet from Johns Hopkins has reintroduced the idea that bed-wetting is usually associated with small bladder capacity. They have urged the training of the child to increase his bladder capacity. A plan for doing this is outlined at the end of this chapter.

Many people feel that bed-wetting can be conquered through conditioning. A special device is used which buzzes if the child wets the bed. This awakens the child. The buzzer treatment has given a thirty per cent cure rate. There are psychiatrists who object to the use of the buzzer because of their "hydraulic theory" of the human psyche. They reason that if you repress one symptom like bed-wetting, the conflict causing it would cause another symptom to pop up.

A great many psychiatrists have come to feel that bed-wetting by itself should not be considered emotional in origin. Unless the bed-wetting is accompanied by some significant difficulty in a major area of living, such as difficulties with parents, playmates, or in school, which are themselves cause for concern, one should not think of bed-wetting as psychologically determined. Only if there are major difficulties which require psychotherapy, in the course of which the bed-wetting disappears, can we consider it to be emotional.

Sometimes children will develop psychological symptoms, secondary to bed-wetting, out of a sense of shame. Parents must never blame the child for bed-wetting because it is out of his control. I have seen children who refused to visit other children in their homes for fear that they might have to sleep there and reveal their "weakness."

WHAT TO DO IF YOUR CHILD WETS HIS BED

First, ask yourself how old he is. Bed-wetting is not considered to be abnormal until after age five. Second, consult a doctor. He will review the symptoms and probably do a urine analysis, to rule out infection, test the concentration of the urine to see if the kidneys can concentrate, examine the urine for sugar and albumin. Chances are he will find everything all right. If everything is fine, that is, there is no evidence of disease, he might want to try one of several methods.

A Method of Increasing Bladder Capacity

It has been common practice to recommend that fluids be restricted, particularly around bedtime, and to wake the child up during the night. I, as have others, find that this method rarely works. For some years there has been interest in the theory that children wet their beds because their bladders are too small to hold the urine at night. This average child may put out from his kidneys something like one half to one ounce an hour of urine, which his bladder has to hold. In the course of the night his bladder may have to hold five to ten ounces. Let us say his bladder can only hold four ounces. It is very likely that as his bladder distends more and more, the urge to urinate will become overwhelming. The idea that one could increase bladder capacity and help bed-wetting has been around for a long time, but recently the theory has been put into practice by many physicians. Actually the method is quite simple, and any parent may try it, at least, without fear of harming the child.

Since we are trying to increase the bladder capacity, we want to do two things:

1. Encourage drinking, rather than discourage it.
2. Encourage the child to hold in his urine as long as he can, actually until it hurts, so as to stretch the bladder.

I do not think that a child of less than six can be expected to do this. Make a game out of it. Ask him during the day to hold in as long as he can. Then have him urinate into a measuring jar. Do this daily. He will of course try to improve his score. One day he may be able to hold in about seven ounces, maybe a week later, eight ounces. Hopefully, gradually he will become dry as his bladder capacity increases. Have him pass urine before he goes to bed, but DO NOT WAKE HIM IN THE MIDDLE OF THE NIGHT. I have found that sometimes the use of a drug such as tincture of belladonna, which tightens the sphincter muscles of the bladder, keeping the urine in, is helpful. I usually start with five drops three times a day increasing by one drop per dose per day, until fifteen drops is reached three times a day. Dryness of the mouth or marked flushing are indications for reducing or eliminating the dosage altogether. Tincture of belladonna should be administered only under a doctor's direction. It goes without saying that your doctor would want to do the tests that I mentioned above before introducing any treatment.

Conditioning Devices

Some children sleep so deeply that they somehow do not perceive signals that their bladder is distended, and, therefore, their sphincters do not clamp down. For such children a conditioning device may be helpful. The device consists of a small metal sheet inserted under the bed sheet and connected to a dry battery. When urine wets the metal, a buzzer goes off, waking the child. Presumably after a month or so of usage, the moment he releases a little urine, he either awakes and his sphincter clamps down on his bladder outlet, or he does this without fully awakening. It does not always work. I knew of one family whose child was using this device. The child did not awake, but the family did. They all got conditioned to awakening at that hour except the patient. After about one month, they stopped using the conditioner so they could sleep through the night again. A year later their boy got over bed-wetting, despite treatment.

Drugs for Bed-wetting

I mentioned tincture of belladonna. Drugs such as benzedrine have been used in an effort to lighten sleep. Tranquilizers have been used with varying success. Of late a drug by the generic name of imapramine hydrochloride has been most successful. It has caused improvement in two-thirds of the children on whom it has been tried. My own experience with it has been most encouraging. There are very rare side effects that your doctor will be familiar with. He of course will have to make the decision as to whether to use it.

Regardless of whether treatment works, remember, bed-wetting of itself is not serious. Have your doctor rule out organic causes. If there are none, do not worry. The child will probably outgrow it. To the parents of an eneuretic child, HAPPINESS IS A DRY BED.

THE STRATEGY OF
DISCIPLINE

════════════════════

HAVE THE POETS DECEIVED YOU?

Are you one of the many American parents who have been severely disillusioned by the actuality of having a family? Has the purity of your abstractions about child-rearing been muddied by experience? You are not alone. Magazines, books, televisions, and radio are the media used by myriads of experts all purporting to have the system, the only proper system, for rearing children. As if this were not enough, theoreticians have tried to show how it is not possible for most of us to be parents at all. Witness the statement by Dr. Margaret Mahler, as quoted by Dr. Chess *et al*, in their book *Your Child Is a Person:* "Mothers who are trying to bring up children normally in spite of their own unconscious conflicts about their maternal role . . . are indeed in a predicament."

Jean-Paul Sartre in his autobiography states, "There is no good father, that's the rule." Later he states, "Had my father lived, he would have crushed me. As luck would have it, he died young."

Now you parents have the picture: theories you cannot follow; unconscious processes you cannot control, impeding motherhood; and the problem of simply surviving fatherhood. All of that is working against you. Is it any wonder that you are frightened?

THE PROBLEM

The problem is one of teaching the child socially acceptable behavior. A civilized human being is an artifice, something that must be contrived out of, or even despite, his nature. Immediately one problem besets us—it is our salvation and perhaps also our undoing—man is not a machine. A machine is a contrivance whose output can be regulated by its input. If man were machine one could predict on the basis of what was done to him what would become of him. It was the theory of the behaviorists that this could be done with men, but it does not work. For the present time, and let us hope for all time, man is not a thing, not a machine.

What does this mean to parents? It means that you cannot control all of the variables; it means that despite your best efforts, things may not turn out the way you want them to. It does not mean, however, that you have to abandon child-rearing to chance. There can at least be a strategy. I shall try in outlining it to avoid cloaking my prejudices in scientific terminology, and to use only those facts about child-rearing that seem to be established.

THE WHO, HOW, WHEN, WHERE OF DISCIPLINE

Who Disciplines Whom?

If I were analyzing the running of a ball club, I would want to know who the players are and who the coach is. Disciplining children to play the game of life is not unlike teaching baseball. Let us start with the coach. The parents —what are they like?

I need not stress how important the personality of the parent is. More important than any techniques of parents is their warmth. The cold, rejecting, non-giving type of mother, the antithesis of the warm, yielding flexible mother, will find the most behavior problems in her children.

How to Be Warm

I will not pretend that there are not individual factors in our personal history and in our temperaments that determine our warmth. But the warmth we are endowed with can be diminished by anxiety. A naturally warm person—I find most mothers to be that way—can become rejecting and cold if she is guilt-ridden and anxious. I do not think the experts have helped. Many parents are so preoccupied with doing the right thing, are so frightened by the possibility of error, that they became anxious. Anxiety, or fear, makes one withdraw into a shell. Who among us has not been so scared that he could hardly talk, or was barely aware of the presence of someone else's feelings, so preoccupied was he with his own?

Now my proposition is quite simple. Throughout this book I have stressed that very often there is no single right way. That may scare you at first, but eventually it should relieve you. Secondly, I should like to stress that there is rarely one single thing that you can do that will be so traumatic as to mark the child for life. Do not feel so guilty if you haul off and smack him or lose your temper and scream once in a while. He will survive. If toilet-training should be difficult, or a sleep problem should develop, all is not lost.

Thirdly, childhood is not everything. Although the first few years of life are important in shaping the personality of the child, subsequent events can change it a great deal. I have no doubt that economic and social forces are increasingly diminishing the effectiveness of the family. The ability of many young adolescents to secure well-paying jobs or government scholarships, as well as the influence of community projects such as nursery schools, youth centers, and guidance clinics, have all tended to decrease the importance of the home in shaping the personality. It is ironic that we chastise parents on the one hand for not being able to control their children and on the other hand that we develop so many projects to keep children out of the home.

Television has undoubtedly played a significant role, too. If it is true, as some reports state, that the average child spends twenty-four hours a week watching television and two hours a week talking with his father, surely he is learning many of his values from that tiny screen.

The general breakdown in authority has seen the rise in influence of the peer group. It pains me to say this, but nevertheless it is true. *The New York Times* reported that 40 per cent of the students at a California college have smoked marijuana. Surely no theory based on parent-child relationships is adequate to explain this, much less correct it.

In summary, dear parents, what you do is not as important, alas, as you think it is.

Who Is Being Disciplined?

In my judgment, parents are not sufficiently aware of the types of natures that their children may be born with. I am referring to inborn temperamental variations that run like threads through their entire lives. These factors have been very well described by Drs. Chess, Thomas, and Birch in their book *Your Child Is a Person*, a book, I might add, that is very worthwhile reading. The result of their ten-year study demonstrated that certain behavioral characteristics remained constant from earliest infancy to later childhood. They existed despite different parental attitudes. The parent cannot change these basic qualities. He must, as the good coach does, learn to manage these characteristics. Here are the nine characteristics that were found in this study.

1. *Activity Level.* Babies from birth on vary in their activities. I have often heard a nurse in the newborn nursery say, "Baby Snyder is very active, she is all over the bassinet," or, "Baby Brown is very quiet. She is fine, but she does not move around much." Now if one follows these children through childhood, the likelihood is that baby Snyder will be one hell of an active two-year-old and baby Brown will not. I usually call the active ones kickers, in contrast to the quiet ones who are lookers or suckers. I can remember, one time in a clinic, a two-year-old running up and down the corridors while waiting to be examined. His mother grasped him firmly by the shoulders shook him violently, and shouted, "Why can't you ever si still?" Forgetting for the moment that violent shaking and yelling are not apt to quiet anybody down, the probability is that this child literally could not sit still—indeed should

not be expected to do so. His carburetor just is not adjusted that way. Maybe your child is a dynamo, maybe a slowly timed metronome. In either event there he is; he is all yours.

2. *Regularity*. Speaking of metronomes brings us to the next quality, regularity. Some children are born with better biological clocks, circadian systems, than others. Some babies will wake up every four hours, almost to the minute, for their feedings, or they will have their bowel movements at approximately the same time each day. These babies naturally do well on the so-called demand schedule. Obviously they are easier to toilet train. If you have the irregular type, you may have a time for yourself before you learn to pattern him. So if your neighbor's baby seems so good, it may not be because of her—it may be her genes.

3. *Approach or Withdrawal as a Characteristic Response*. Drs. Chess, Thomas, and Birch found that each child had its own consistent response to a new situation. Some children had a devil-may-care attitude, others were exceedingly cautious. I am sort of an expert in the latter type. Both of my children, when brought into a room full of strangers, would cling to their Mother—I was not good enough—put their thumbs in their mouths and lower their eyes. I suffered the silent accusations of my guests. That monster that I was, I had raised inhibited children. "And he is a pediatrician yet." Thanks to the findings of the good doctors we understood that we had done our children no grievous harm. What is more, we learned that they were not really shy. Once they warmed up to the situation they enjoyed themselves immensely.

4. *Adaptability to Change in Routine*. There is no doubt that some infants are conservative by nature. They adopt the principle that nothing new should be tried for the first time. These infants resist shifts from breast to bottle, from bottle to cup, from formula exclusively to solids. They require patience and persistence. For example, if you should wish to change their nap hour to fit in better with your schedule, you may find it difficult.

The mother of such a child, after several months of struggling over this and that finally came into the office with a look of triumph. "Well, you seemed to have made it," I said. "How did you do it?" "Well, I learned that I had to adapt to her, she did not have to adapt to me."

"We surrendered to the land, and the land was ours," says a poem by Robert Frost. In short, if you can't lick 'em join 'em. The important thing is to recognize it when you have one of these children and to make up your minds that he will always be like that. You will either have to have patience in repeating what you want done, until he slowly yields, or give in to him. Don't get angry at him. Ask your mother, you were probably like that yourself.

5. *Level of Sensory Threshold.* There are some children who could sleep if a brass band was playing "Hail to the Chief" in their room; there are others who would awake with a start if you whispered, "Shhh, be quiet, I don't want to wake the baby." Each child varies in his response to stimuli. This carries over to later life. I have known children to respond with tears to a subtle, slightly forbidding change in voice, and others whom you would have to hit over the head just to get their attention.

6. *Positive or Negative Mood.* Dr. Chess and her associates found that there was a fairly consistent quality to a child's mood. Some children have a sort of base line of high spirits. Others are generally more somber. Once upon a time there were twins who were identical, except for their mood. One seemed always happy, the other was dour. In order to test the consistency of this mood, the following experiment was run. A room was filled with horse manure. The dour twin was put in the room. The door was closed. One half hour later the door was unlocked. The child came out his face reflecting his usual unhappy reaction. "How did you like it?" he was asked. "What's there to like?" he replied. The happy twin was next locked into the same room. Through the door they could hear him whistling and singing. They could not understand it. When he came out they asked him what he was so happy about. "Of course I was happy," he said. "With all the manure in there, there must be a pony somewhere."

What this apocryphal story illustrates is true. Individuals vary in their general moods. It may take some getting used to, particularly if you have the dour type. Once again the important thing is to recognize it.

7. *Intensity of Response.* "When he is hungry he lets you know it," a perceptive mother of three said to me above the sound of loud, furious bellowing issuing from her four-month-old. "He is different from my daughter. She is so even-tempered. She does not get mad easily. She

may cry a little when she is hungry, but she is not nearly so impatient as he is." This mother recognized the inherent differences between her children and responded accordingly. She knew her onions and her pears.

8. *Distractability*. I have known children who could persist in doing their homework in a room with the television blaring and constant intrusions by younger brothers and sisters. "He can work anywhere," a proud mother said to me. "I never worry about him." I have known the other type, too. A dripping faucet or the hum of a vacuum cleaner is enough to distract them from their work. These differences are probably inherent. One can follow these threads of behavior from infancy. The child who in infancy persists in sucking on his bottle without interruption when the phone rings becomes the toddler who will not be distracted from what he wants, no matter what his mother tries, and grows into the student who can concentrate anywhere. The infant who is easily distracted from his eating years later is easily distracted from his work. The parent, aware of this, soon learns that the latter needs a quiet place to eat and his own study if possible.

9. *Persistency*. We usually refer to this as "stick-to-itiveness." All of us are aware of the variations in this quality. Give one child a clothespin, and he will play with it for hours. Give another a wonderful electric car, and it will amuse him for a short time before he is off doing something else. The former, I suspect, is the type of child who might develop hobbies like stamp collecting and could stay in his room for hours, examining and placing stamps in albums. The latter are more flighty, starting one thing and then starting another. I have known several of the latter types who, as they grew older, could read several books at the same time, dropping one, say a biography, picking up a story, and then running through an encyclopedia.

Both types of behavior have virtue, both have drawbacks. Once again, make an assessment of whom you are dealing with.

How

If you accept my thesis that most behavior is learned, and that instinct is relatively less important in the human than in other species, we immediately face the problem of how best to teach. Notice, I am avoiding any moralistic position. I am not saying that children should respect their parents and must do what they are told. Not at all. I am interested in teaching socially acceptable behavior. A wise friend of mine stated that he operated on the assumption that he knew more than any two-year-old. A fair assumption, no?

Children learn by imitating. They watch and learn. A child learns best if he has someone to identify with. We think that little girls learn to behave like girls because they identify with their mothers. Hopefully little boys identify with their fathers. They learn because they are motivated to do so. After they have made the identification, parental pressure for achievement rewarding the achievement, association with a fair degree of success rather than too frequent experiencing of the frustration of failure will result in positive motivation. In everyday terms, if you want a particular form of response, ask a child what is possible, and reward him when he accomplishes it. I do not mean that every single time he blows his nose you are to applaud and present him with a gift. But if he behaves politely, you might comment on it favorably. When you wish to encourage or discourage a particular form of behavior, be specific. Let us say he pulled the lamp cord. Do not say, "Kid, you are driving me mad. You're a very bad boy." He may not know what you are talking about. Be specific. Say, "I do not want you to touch that lamp cord." Say it firmly, as if you mean it. You may have to say it a couple of times, particularly if he is the persistent type. Remember whom you are addressing.

SOME DONT'S

Don't try to teach by seduction. Let me give you an example. Mary Jane does not like carrots. You want her to eat carrots. (Why, I do not know, but anyway you want her to eat carrots.) When she refuses, you say, "But Mary Jane you know you like carrots. All your friends like carrots. Betsy eats carrots, Celeste eats carrots, Debbie eats carrots." Actually you have not taken a poll, but somehow you are going to seduce her into eating carrots.

Let us say you have continued this method for some years. Your daughter is now 16. She comes and asks whether she can go out on a date with an 18-year-old boy

who has his own car. You say no. She replies, "But Betsy's
mother allows her to go, Celeste's mother allows her to go,
and what's more Debbie's mother allows her to go." You
reply, somewhat vexed, "I don't give a damn what anyone
else does." There it goes—a lesson of a lifetime shot to
pieces.

In summary, be direct. And what's so important about
carrots anyway?

Don't use harsh physical punishment if you can avoid
it. There is fairly conclusive evidence that hard physical
punishment seems to increase exactly the behavior that
you are trying to discourage. It is quite clear that if your
child is aggressive, more than you like, physical punishment will make him more so. Let us say that he hits other
children in the playground. You start hitting him for it.
The chances are that he will not only keep hitting the
other children, he will start hitting you back.

Don't think I am going to leave you in the playground
with that monster. The thing to do is to pull him away
firmly when he starts hitting, making it clear that you do
not like it. If he spends an afternoon without hitting, let
him know you like it and why; if he persists in hitting,
you may have to avoid the playground for a while. If he is
old enough, you can encourage him to be peaceable by rewarding him. This is not bribery. It is a good psychological principle of reinforcement. I warned you not to moral-
ize anyway.

Let us take a contrary example. Your child of three is
too dependent on you. He clings to you in the playground.
When other children come around he hides behind your
skirt. That's an image that will arouse you, won't it? You
feel like socking him. "He is such a baby." I know, believe
me, I know. Don't. It will not get you anywhere. Worse
yet it will make him more dependent. Live with it a while.
Play it cool. Forget what other people tell you. Resist the
impulse to sock him. Little by little he will become more
aggressive, but within his own limitations. Remember
whom you are dealing with.

Mild methods of discipline and a low pressure technique
are more likely to be effective than harsh, high-pressure
methods. I admit at first glance it seems illogical. It may
not seem so after I acquaint you with the theory of dissonance and its application to child-rearing. This theory, developed by Dr. Leon Festinger, has it that when a person

holds two conflicting ideas simultaneously, tension, or dissonance, occurs. The person subjected to this tension may use various techniques to reduce the tension.

How does this apply to discipline? Let me cite an example of how this works from an article by Professor Elliot Aronson. Suppose a child likes to beat up his little brother, and you want to stop him. Probably the best way to get him to stop is to hit him hard. The more severe the threat, the greater the likelihood that he will stop. However, he may very well hit his brother again the minute you turn your back.

Suppose, instead, you threaten him with a very mild punishment, a punishment which is just barely severe enough to get him to stop fighting. In either case—under the threat of severe or of mild punishment—the child is experiencing dissonance. He is aware that he is not beating up his little brother while also aware that he wants to. When his little brother is present the child has the urge to beat him up, and when he refrains he asks himself in effect, "How come I am not beating up my little brother?" Under severe threat he has a ready answer. "I am not beating up my little brother because if I do that giant (my father) standing there is going to knock hell out of me." In fact, the threat of severe punishment provides a child with justification for not beating up his brother at the moment—when he is being watched.

But consider the child in the mild threat situation. He experiences dissonance (tension), too. When he asks himself, "How come I am not beating up my little brother," the difference is that he does not have a good answer because the threat was so mild (the loss of candy for example) that it does not provide complete justification for having stopped. He must find other supporting reasons for not hitting his little brother. He can convince himself that he really does not like to beat his brother up, that he did not want to do it in the first place.

To show that this theory works, Dr. Aronson devised a series of experiments in which he exposed children to a group of toys. One group of children were threatened with severe punishment if they played with a particular toy. They still felt the toy was desirable, the forbidden fruit. Another group were mildly threatened, and they placed a lesser value on the toy and were thus less likely to want to play with it.

All this is by way of saying that it is better not to yell, "Georgie, I'll break your head if you do that again." Rather disapprove mildly but firmly by saying, "George, I would rather you didn't." Try it—it's a switch anyway.

When

"I'm afraid that if I don't teach him to hold the cup now, he never will."

"He is so lazy, he won't walk for me."

These two remarks I have selected at random to illustrate parental pressures and consequent pitfalls in dealing with infant development. There is fairly clear evidence that encouraging a child to do something before the age of physical readiness may actually impede his ability. If I try to push a ten-month-old or even a year-old child to walk before he is ready, I might actually delay the onset of walking. The average age for walking is about fourteen months. The wise parent would allow for the opportunity to walk but should not force the child to walk.

On the other hand, if one waits too long beyond the age of readiness, there may be difficulties also; let me cite an example: learning to chew. The average child will make chewing movements, regardless of whether he has teeth, at about six months of age. If one withholds chopped foods much beyond this age there is a greater possibility that the child will have difficulty managing chopped foods when they are offered. In my own practice, I introduce chopped foods at about six months of age, and have never seen a child who later gags and refuses solids as is fairly common when chopped foods are not introduced till the child is older.

It is apparent that most of the learning of the more sophisticated types of socially useful behavior depends on the use of language. It is the distinguishing characteristic of our species. It should follow logically that most discipline of the sophisticated sort should not be attempted until after the development of language. I can remember an inexperienced young couple who punished their fourteen-month-old for turning the T.V. set on and off by yelling and screaming at him and making him sit in a corner, striking him if he moved. Now it is possible that when they took him away from the T.V. set, he could understand even at such a young age that at that instant they did not want him to touch it. I don't think it likely that he could understand that he was *never* to touch it. That is a fairly sophisticated concept, involving a sense of time, and certainly involving the language concept. I am not saying that they could not eventually get him to stop touching the T.V. set by their harsh methods. I am saying that they would be accomplishing this at a considerable psychological price. A better way would be to attempt to distract him, if he is that type, to keep the T.V. set out of sight (you really need a console model with doors that close), or to take the knobs off. A modern industrial society, in my view, makes demands on small children they are not ready to accept.

The same holds true for table manners. There is no point in accusing a one-year-old of being messy when he cannot have the faintest notion of what you are talking about. I have discussed toilet-training in another chapter, and hopefully have discouraged harsh teaching methods in that regard.

WHEN AND THE AMERICAN PARADOX

Most cross-cultural surveys indicate, and this may come as a surprise, that in infant handling our culture is more restrictive and less permissive than primitive ones. No Bushman mother puts her child in his own bed in a darkened room and expects him to go to sleep. A Korean physician told me that he had to close down a pediatric ward in his hospital because no mother would leave her child there. I am not trying to say we are wrong or right. I am simply stating a fact: we make more demands on our very young than most cultures.

Why is there a paradox in all this? If we accept the fact that discipline is the learning of socially useful behavior—I think I have belabored that one enough—then it should follow that the demands should be greater as one gets older. The paradox in this country is to be found in the fact that we are relatively more demanding of our young and decrease our demands as our children get older. The end result is the development of an adolescent subculture that does not communicate and won't listen to its elders. I would be the first to admit that there are other factors in this relationship, but the fact that we have got the whole thing backward does not help.

Where

Many parents become angered and frustrated when attempts at discipline fail in public situations. It's when you expect the most and get the least. The lessons of discipline are best learned at home. Some years ago, I heard a story about some parents who had difficulty toilet-training their son. The advice they received from their physician emphasized that if they could once get him in a positive mood when he agreed to sit on the potty, they would have him trained. Consequently they carried around a collapsible potty chair wherever they went, in hopes of catching him in the right mood. Two months later on a visit to their physician, he asked how things were going. "Oh fine," they said with a sad expression, "he is toilet-trained now."

"But you do not seem happy," said the physician.

"Well," they replied, "we have been barred from Howard Johnson's for life."

Some lessons of life are best taught first at home.

POSTSCRIPT

I have found that in general with regard to discipline I can categorize parents into two groups. The first group consists of parents who are afraid of spoiling. The second group, those who are afraid of inhibiting or "traumatizing." If you do not know about traumatizing, you probably belong in the first group. The first group, the fear-of-spoiling group, is too restrictive, and the second group too permissive. Specifically, the first group tends to demand too much too soon. Its members, if they have tried too harshly to suppress aggression, are likely to have children who are too aggressive, or, if they have used force in a misguided effort to encourage independence, they will have children who are too dependent.

The members of the second group usually read all the current literature on child-rearing and tend to be too permissive. Their children might be said to be aggressive by default because they are never discouraged. These are by far the majority in my practice.

I can always recognize such a home. The place is a disorderly mess. Skates, kitchen utensils, shoes, and clothes are dangerously strewn about. If mother is talking, a four-year-old interrupts her by striking her from behind to get attention.

CHILDREN SEEM TO WANT DIRECTION

In a very permissive kindergarten, I heard about the teacher who stood in front of her class and said, "You can all do anything you want to."

A bright five-year-old girl raised her hand and asked, "Do we have to do what we want?"

Parents have to structure some order out of the anarchy of a child's life.

Am I Too Restrictive?

Do you demand that the children keep their rooms clean at all times?

Do you feel that there are certain rooms the children must never go into for fear of ruining the furniture (that you are still paying off)?

Do you think that children should be seen and not heard?

When your little boy falls down and cries do you push him away and tell him, "Act like a man"?

Do you believe in spare the rod and spoil the child?

If your answer to most of these questions is yes, and you are having trouble with toilet-training and aggressive behavior, for example, you may want to ease up a bit. Go ahead and try easing up for at least a couple of weeks. See how it affects the specific form of behavior you are trying to discourage, such as hitting other children. Spare the rod. It might work.

Am I Too Permissive?

Do you feel that some insistence on keeping an orderly room for your six-year-old represents compulsivity on your part?

Do you feel that if your child hits you, it represents "hostility" on his part, and indicates that you have done something wrong?

Are you afraid to encourage him or even to insist firmly

that he sit on the potty seat for fear of giving him a "trauma"?

If, at age two, he refuses to go to sleep without you, do you stay with him until he falls asleep, no matter how long, because you "know" that sleep problems are due to insecurity?

If things are not always going right, do you know that you must be doing something wrong?

If the answers to most of these questions are yes, you are having one hell of a time and maybe one hell of a kid. Tighten up a little. Do not be afraid. Maybe if you take the position that you are bigger than he or she is, he or she will stop hitting you.

Well there it is—there's no easy way. Good luck.

OOH, HE SAID
A NAUGHTY WORD

Any advice that I can give on this subject is predicated on the parental attitude to naughty words. This can be no better illustrated than by the following incident.

Some years ago, while I was working on the ward of a big city hospital, I was witness to an interplay between a six-year-old boy, his nurse, and his mother. The youngster was recuperating from pneumonia, and his doctor suggested that each afternoon he get an extra glass of milk to help build him up. On the first afternoon the nurse presented the milk to the child, and he ignored it. The nurse became gently insistent, at which point the boy turned to her and said, "You can take that goddamned glass of milk away." The nurse managed to contain herself and left with the glass of milk.

The following day she approached the boy in a bright, breezy, confident manner and urged the milk on him. "You can take that goddamned milk away," he said again. Again the nurse contained herself and managed not to react. She removed the milk without comment. The following day she brought him the milk again. She had just managed to place it on his bedside table when, once again, he said, "You can take that goddamned milk away." This time the nice nurse could not really contain herself. "Naughty, naughty," she said, "I am going to tell your mother when she comes."

That evening at visiting hours the nurse went up to the mother. She was somewhat embarrassed to tell her what happened, but she felt it her duty. "When I put the milk down in front of him he says, 'You can take that god-damned milk away.'" "Well," said the mother, "if he doesn't want the goddamned milk, the hell with him."

The kind of language that your child uses is, in one way or another, learned. It may be learned from you, and there is no sense being surprised by that, or it may be learned from playmates, which isn't surprising either.

Very often a child will use a word that he doesn't know the meaning of. He is using the word for effect. Naturally, if he gets the desired effect—for example, getting you flustered—he will repeat it. In those circumstances, it's best to "deadpan it," and the child probably won't repeat it.

It's quite another matter when a child of five or six knows in general what the word connotes. I think in that instance it's best to react to it the way you feel. If you are shocked by his language you'd better let him know. If you are not, but you would prefer he not use that particular language, you better make the appropriate response. I my-self don't, as is advised in some baby books, believe in act-ing out a kind of charade. Don't pretend that you are not shocked if you are. Don't play shocked if you are not. Children can sense the truth of things. Worse than having a swearing child is a child who thinks his parents are hyp-ocrites.

My rule is, "No goddamned kid of mine is going to use naughty words."

HOW TO GET YOUR CHILD
HOME WITHOUT CALLING HIM

When your youngster reaches five or six years of age, he will probably be reluctant to return home for dinner and will want to stay out with his playmates, particularly if he is having a good time.

According to some authorities, there is danger in direct action such as calling, "Hey, Brucie, come on home." These authorities believe that when the youngster is participating in a group situation he is actually allowing his ego to mix with the other little egos of his playmates. If you call him at this point, you suddenly make him aware of his own little ego which is diffusing with the other little egos. The child, say the authorities, in attempting to extricate his ego from the group may do it hastily and leave part of it there. This results in a sense of incompleteness.

A better idea is to get the youngster to *want* to come home. One way of doing this is the Children's Cocktail Hour. If the child knows that when he returns home each afternoon at about five-thirty he may have a cocktail like Mommy and Daddy do, this will make him feel grown up and compensate him for the ego loss.

When mothers tell me of their problems in retrieving children at the end of the day, I have some radical advice for them which may appall the authorities. I suggest they tell the child before he goes out that he will be called in at a certain hour. Even if he can't tell time yet or hasn't got a watch, he will know that the hour has arrived by hearing your voice calling him. If he doesn't respond (and you have previously ascertained that he doesn't have an organic hearing problem), *go out there and get him.* As a result of the need for this extra effort, deprive him of something, say the chance to go back to his friends after dinner. (What kind of friends are they anyway, don't they have homes to go to and dinners to eat?)

The thing to remember about authorities is that when Columbus first came here he thought he found India. True, he did find something. What I find is that direct action like "Brucie, come home!" works wonders. If nothing else, it gives Brucie an authority to come home to.

HOW TO CAMP OUT
WITH THE KIDS, OR
HOW NOT TO BE A SQUARE PARENT

There is a definite strain between the generations, caused in part by the problem of communication. The following expressions are so outdated that their use will cause your children to think of you as way out, or not with it. If you insist on using them, you may hear, "Mother, you're right off the wall," or, "Dad, you're from Weirdsville."

If you are over thirty and have a child over three, you are in grave danger of camping out if you use:

Naughty, you were naughty. Most kids hardly know what the word means, and if they do, it has little impact.

It's beddy-bye time. This is sure to provoke knowing smiles and resistance to sleep. Say, "Get the heck to bed." They will understand.

Finish your yum-yum. This is so far out it makes me lose my appetite. How about you?

When I was. . . . Any sentence that begins with "When I was . . . ," "When I was your age . . . ," "When I was a boy . . . ," as soon as uttered makes you a dead duck.

Stockings. When I was a boy (there, I did it), stockings were bisexual. Now stockings are for girls and socks are for boys.

Sentences that begin with, "Don't you ever . . ."

Don't you ever listen to the radio?
Don't you ever read?

Don't you ever stop chewing gum?
Don't you ever get a haircut?
Don't you ever polish your shoes?

Victrola. Kids do not know what a victrola is. Use record player.

Machine. Never use this word for auto.

What is the magic word? When you try to teach your child to say please, use a more direct approach. I know some parents who asked their child, "What is the magic word?" and were quite shocked by the answer.

Expressions that begin with "I'll bet . . ." Such as, "I'll bet Judith wouldn't do that."

"I'll bet if you had to work the way I did when I
was your age . . . (a double camp out)."
"I'll bet you think money grows on trees."

You needn't switch from your generation's vocabulary to that of your children. If they simply know that you know their words and use your own *by choice,* that's fine. Incidentally, if you hear a child use a word and you're not sure of the meaning, *ask.* It's great for a kid's pride to teach a parent something for a change!

WHAT YOU CAN TEACH
YOUR CHILDREN ABOUT SEX
WITHOUT UNDUE EMBARRASSMENT

There is no doubt that patterns of sexual behavior are changing, particularly among the middle class. My own guess is that this has something to do with the industrial revolution, the automobile, the motel, the movies—especially outdoor movies, changing censorship laws, good nutrition, and the waning influence of the family.

What has not changed is the influence of the endocrine glands. It is awfully hard to combat the effect of the endocrine glands. I, myself, am not one of those who think that night baseball will ever replace sex. On the other hand I think that if a law were passed in this country outlawing the double bed and making twin beds mandatory, it would be an effective step in decreasing sexual activity. Sex indulgence is partly glandular, partly opportunity, and partly convenience.

How shall we teach the kids about it?

I suspect that many children learn about sex the way I did. I learned from the older kids on the block, from graffiti in the men's room, and ultimately in a visit to a brothel as part of my fraternity pledging. As a young, modern parent, I was utterly opposed to these haphazard ways. I believed in the orderly process of learning. Accordingly, when my daughter at age nine asked how babies were conceived, naturally I did not give her the stork bit (children nowadays have never seen a stork, so it is pointless). With the verbal help of my wife, I tried to tell her what men and women do to beget children. My daughter listened, smiled, and said, "That's odd." It is odd, and it is certainly funny in a way—sex, that is. I guess she did not take it too seriously.

Most modern parents take sex too seriously. I don't, and I find that many psychiatrists agree (there I go, hiding behind authority again). I do not think that sexual behavior is necessarily connected with the character of a person, the way orthodox Freudians do. I do not think it is necessarily connected with love either, the way the "loveniks" do. I think if you inquire about the sexual behavior of an adult, you are going to learn mainly how he spends twenty minutes once in a while. As a physician, I have been exposed to enough information in print and in person to be convinced that the varieties of sexual behavior are probably infinite, and I feel that adults ought to be allowed to engage in any activity that doesn't frighten the horses in the street.

Notice I am talking about adults. I think that it is the adults who need the sexual education, not the children. My point is that there has been a great deal of confusion about sex because we haven't regarded sexual behavior as the arbitrary choice that it is. We haven't made clear that adults, I stress adults, have choices to make. Children should not be allowed to make choices in sexual behavior; what's more, they shouldn't be placed in the position where they might be tempted to do what we, as adults, decide they ought not to do. Notice I am not talking about biological drives or the harmful psychological effects of repression. I am not abandoning my right to determine how my children behave.

To be perfectly realistic, I don't expect them to behave the way I would like now and forever; they are subject not only to other influences, but to the sheer contrariness which makes every generation react against its elders. However, I would try to *influence* my children as much as I can. When it comes to sex, though, I sometimes feel like a voice in the dark. We teach teenagers how to drive cars and then give them the cars to commit mayhem with. With sex, they have the instincts and the instruments ready; the trend of the times is to give them the license and the other equipment they may need. Where will this all lead to?

THE THEORY OF THE DRY RUN

Many psychiatrists and some pediatricians have reasoned that since the sex drive is instinctual, it should not be repressed. They say that since the "drive" is there, and since suppressing it may produce neurosis, the best thing to do is to teach young people how to handle themselves. They are the ones who would argue that birth control pills be handed out to college girls via the college health office and that young men should receive complete instruction in birth control just in case their girl friends are unprepared.

Let's follow this logically. Give the college students all the help they need or want (if they don't want it, expose them to it anyway). And since so many high school girls are ending up in maternity wards, let's give them courses in high school, too. To continue with this logic one ought also to teach sex very candidly in grade school. Wouldn't it actually be better to let grade school kids practice sex with each other before they are biologically mature so that they can practice çoolly and dispassionately without fear of mishap that may lead to pregnancy? Since practice makes perfect, by the time they reach puberty they will be skilled sexualists who can have sex safely right through high school, college, and old age. Logic ought to carry us even further because we now know all about infantile sexuality. Nevertheless, however modern parents may be, even if both parents are orthodox Freudians, perhaps even orthodox Freudian analysts, I don't see that they can do anything more than let a boy baby and a girl baby take an occasional ride in a baby carriage together. I call this the theory of the dry run.

I think we have to be cautious about "inexorable laws" in regard to sex. (Death, taxes, yes, but not sex.) For instance, we hear a great deal about the harm of sexual repression. The case may not be all that clear cut. Let me illustrate. The Japanese woman is, or maybe was, one of the most repressed that we know of. Her choice of a mate was not hers. Certainly she could not be "free" in expressing her feelings. She had little to say about her sexual behavior. Yet there is no evidence that the incidence of neurosis or psychosis or even plain unhappiness was any greater in the Japanese women of yesterday than in the American woman of today. Now, I'm not saying that Japanese behavior ought to be a model for us. I am saying that there may be no natural laws that we can fall back on to guide us with certainty. This applies to our children and our adolescents. We have, I think, the right to tell them how we want them to behave. We have the right to structure their situations to modify their behavior. My main point is that we can do this with confidence that we are not doing them any grievous injury.

There is no sense in preaching to your son or daughter —I am, of course, preaching to you—if you are going to allow them to get into situations where they cannot be expected to follow, or even to remember, your teaching. In other words, if you allow your son to have a couple of beers with his girl friend, pack tight, skin to skin, in the back seat of a convertible, while their glands ooze, don't expect them to remember your admonition about not going too far—and I don't mean away from home. I think it's about time that somebody drove the bus.

Someone, us that is, must decide how we want our children and adolescents to behave. It is your decision. At least you can try in a direct, forceful manner, if that is the way you choose.

I have reached the following conclusions based on contact with my patients and their parents.

The modern child is very unlikely to suffer from the sense of guilt and shame that previous generations were purported to. The average child knows a lot more about sex than his parent thinks he does. He is very likely to obtain the information anyway, no matter what you do. If he asks questions, answer them directly. But answer only what he asks. Don't give him any more information than he needs. Don't give him a long lecture on how natural it is, and then be surprised when he's acting naturally. In other words, don't be a hypocrite.

As far as behavior is concerned, make it clear how you feel you want him or her to behave. Don't worry about repression. After you've done all that—pray.

THE CURE OF
TEENAGE SMOKING

The teenager sitting and watching T.V. is confronted with the following scene:

A young, virile, handsome man and a beautiful, curvaceous girl are walking hand in hand along a beach. They stop . . . gaze seaward. The young man lights a cigarette for his companion and himself, they puff, somewhat erotically, and the announcer makes his pitch for that particular brand. The teenager watching identifies smoking with romance, youth, and health. Despite restrictions imposed on cigarette advertisers, teenage smoking is on the rise. It has become an increasingly serious problem.

My plan to cut down on teenage smoking would be to use the capacity for identification negatively. Suppose the anti-smoker forces prepared the following T.V. advertisement:

The tiny screen is filled with the picture of a Hassidic Jew. He is bearded, of course. He is wearing a somewhat oversized black hat, his white shirt is stained with egg, and he is tieless. His teeth are yellow and unevenly arranged. He is puffing on a cigarette, and as he finishes, he says, "By me it's Camels."

I have a feeling we would get a lot of teenagers to stop smoking.

I have to admit that this plan to stop teenagers from smoking is impractical. Even if we could raise the money for such a campaign, I doubt that we could get by the Anti-Defamation League. Nevertheless, I feel that the principle holds true. Teenagers smoke because it makes them feel sophisticated, tough, and independent—all feelings that they strive for. Also, in some smokers an adrenalinlike substance is produced in the brain, giving them a lift.

I think, however, that it is incontrovertible that smoking is related to lung cancer, aggravates certain forms of heart disease, and is associated with a higher rate of low-birthweight babies in cigarette-smoking mothers.

My own view is that smoking, like any other dangerous activity, should be legally restricted for the young. Adults, of course, should have the option of smoking after they have been presented with the facts. Adults, in my society, should have privileges, even privileges to make mistakes, that children should not. Otherwise, what is the advantage of growing up?

In the area where I practice, there is a college which forbids its students to smoke and invokes severe penalties, including long confinement to the campus, for violations. I know of one student there who says he hates smoking, gets no pleasure from it, but has gotten the habit just because it is so strictly forbidden. Similarly, you can try to enforce strict rules about smoking for your own teenagers, but what will they do behind your back?

Children, including teenage children, are probably more susceptible than adults to facts because they spend so much of their lives in an environment of learning. I think a useful approach is to sit down with a child of twelve or thirteen, before he is likely to be tempted to smoke, and to explain all the facts now available to us. Smoking, you can tell him, is physiologically habit-forming. Cigarettes contain nicotine, a drug, and once the drug is taken for a while, the body craves its dose of nicotine, especially after meals. You might explain that playing it safe by not inhaling, a frequent beginner's practice, is not safe at all because most of the nicotine is absorbed through the lining of the mouth (that is why pipe and cigar smokers can satisfy their nicotine addiction without inhaling). Most teenagers yearn for independence, so putting smoking in the context of non-independence, that is being a slave to a habit, might help if they understand how the habit develops and how hard it is to break.

Male as well as female youngsters are interested in their appearance. You might point out that smoking inevitably stains the teeth yellow.

You can tell them what science has learned about smoking in recent years, that it *does* have an effect on the heart (that is why athletes are sometimes forbidden to smoke), and seems definitely related to the incidence of lung cancer.

If you are with your twelve- or thirteen-year-old and you pass youngsters smoking, ask if he thinks the kids are really big shots because they smoke. The point will register.

Lastly, some children are very influenced by money, and you might point out that if a carton of cigarettes costs, say, three dollars, and they smoke a carton a week for the next fifty years, they are choosing to let $7,800 go up in smoke! You'd be surprised how effective that argument can be with children who are respectful of nickels and dimes.

While you are telling them all this, if you are a smoker too, rally all of your histrionic talent, smoke and cough away, roll your eyes and look thoroughly disgraceful. You'll make them ashamed to smoke.

HOW TO GET MORE MILEAGE
OUT OF YOUR PEDIATRICIAN

One night my phone rang at 3 A.M. The voice at the other end of the telephone was wavering, but doing its best to control itself. Its owner was a young mother who announced, "My baby had a green stool." I inquired how the baby seemed otherwise. Was his color good, did he seem to be breathing all right, was he alert? She said that everything seemed fine. I then asked her what made her call at this hour. She said, "Dr. Spock says that if your baby has a green stool, you should call the Doctor." I asked her why she had not called Dr. Spock. Freud said that there is a hostility in humor or attempts at it. I think it was the mildest response I could have made under the circumstances.

Actually, my feelings in a situation like this are mixed. I could understand her anxiety, in this case fostered by a book, but I am human, too. Like most of my colleagues, I like to sleep once in a while. The average pediatrician has about 1000 patients. Suppose that a mother of each of those patients called after midnight, once every three years. From Mother's point of view, calling once in a three-year period at 3 A.M. does not seem like much. From the pediatrician's point of view, it could mean that he would be called every night after midnight for three years. Do you follow my mathematics?

WHEN TO CALL THE DOCTOR: THE REAL EMERGENCIES

In thinking back, I would say that the major reasons for calling a pediatrician at any time of the day or night are few. Of course, there are certain bona fide emergencies. They are firstly and most commonly *breathing difficulties*. An infant or child who wakes with breathing difficulty, that is, who has trouble inhaling, probably has croup. The parent should try steaming him, either with a cold steam vaporizer—this is preferable—or by bringing him into the bathroom which has been steamed up by running the hot shower full blast. If there is no relief, or the child seems bad to begin with, the doctor should be called.

Obviously a child who is *bleeding*, and the bleeding cannot be stopped, should see a doctor. You may be better off getting him to the emergency room of a hospital where there is equipment available to stop bleeding. Your doctor would probably suggest this if you called him.

Severe abdominal pain, if it persists for more than an hour or two, is something for a doctor to know about. I am not talking about the child who wakes up and says his stomach hurts. In about fifteen minutes, he will seem better. This kind of nondescript pain is fairly frequent. In simpler days we used to call it a bellyache.

A *stupor* is a state of loginess, the mind and senses dulled. A *coma* is a state of unconsciousness from which the child cannot be awakened, as he always can from sleep. A *convulsion* is the uncontrolled movement of the limbs and a general trembling of the body. Any of these conditions calls for immediate medical attention.

You will have noticed that I started off by protesting that some people called doctors needlessly at 3 A.M., and then I immediately listed some of the important reasons why you ought to call us no matter what time of the day or night. You see we are not such a bad lot of fellows.

When you are involved with another human being, you are involved in a dialogue. It is the *I* and *THOU* relationship, not the *I* and *IT* relationship. The indication that the relationship between patient and doctor has changed through the years is to be observed in the language we employ. Nobody referring to a doctor fifty years ago would say "I *use* Dr. Rogers." You use a thing, but you cannot use another human being. Sometimes use means abuse.

I do not intend this to be a polemic against people, who happen to be patients, but thanks for listening. I feel better now.

WHEN NOT TO CALL THE DOCTOR

"Jeffrey has a cold," Mother announces over the phone. This announcement of fact is presumably to be responded to by a recitation from the pediatrician which includes some new remedy for a cold. It is with deep regret that I must state that there has been nothing new for colds for perhaps 50 years. The best treatment I know is the hat treatment. This unfortunately cannot be applied to children, but it may be of some help to you when you have a cold. The first thing to do is to get a four-poster bed. Hang a hat on one of the posters. Next get a bottle of cognac. Keep drinking the cognac until you see two hats. The moral is, if you have a cold, relax and enjoy it.

Sometimes I think that pediatricians are put through the same trials that novitiates in Zen Buddhism go through. In Zen one is asked *coans,* sort of unanswerable questions that are supposed to free the individual from rational thought. For example, "What is the meaning of Mu?" or "What is the sound of one hand clapping?" A *coan* often asked of pediatricians by parents is in the form of a statement, "I think that Linda may be coming down with a cold." Mind you, not a frank outright cold about which you can do nothing curative anyway, but merely the suspicion of the possibility of such an event. I suppose the difficulty is that parents think there is something you can do to "nip a cold in the bud." Well, there is no nipping, unless it is done by the pediatrician out of sheer frustration. Most pediatricians I know would rather be faced with a case of meningitis, where their training and skill become important, than to be bedeviled by the unanswerable. Leave the poor guy alone; he cannot do anything much about a cold, much less an incipient cold.

I have sometimes been asked to diagnose a rash that appeared the day before yesterday and has now disappeared. "He had a rash yesterday, and now it is gone; what was it?" It is hard enough to diagnose rashes that are present without attempting retrospectively over the telephone to diagnose one that has gone away.

There is another sort of question I call the mousetrap —which I have learned to side step. It goes like this: "Are carrots good for diarrhea?" The innocent physician displaying his knowledge says sure they are; they contain pectine, which is binding, and potassium, which is sometimes lost from the body in diarrhea. Even though partially digested carrots appear in the stool, they are nevertheless helpful. "Well, she won't eat carrots." So what can he do?

No one food is important in anything, so why ask?

Another example of the mousetrap question is: "How much sleep should Billy get?" Anyone who has had any experience in practicing pediatrics will see that trap a mile away. He should reply with a question, "How much sleep does Billy get?" If it is a reasonable amount and the child does not appear unusually tired during the day, the pediatrician will reply that is fine. The amount of sleep children require is extremely variable, as it is in adults.

There are questions better left unasked. Now do not take me amiss. Answering questions is part of the trade, and we accept that. I am suggesting, however, that if you wish to get more mileage out of us, you try to spare us once in a while.

Being a pediatrician has its rewards. It is gratifying to be able to answer questions computer fashion that cover the range from "Does he have the plague?" to "Do you believe in rubber pants?" I think no one is in a better position to see the enormous changes in child-rearing practices, the rising tide of expectations for happiness and good health that so differentiates this generation of parents from its predecessors. We see, too, how this quest for health and happiness has its drawbacks in frustrations on ours and parents' parts in our inability to answer all questions or to guarantee well-being. The gulf between expectations and the ability of science to fulfill those expectations is still quite wide. It is in this context that I try, as do most of my fellow physicians, to understand parents' questions—not literally, but as part of the social change out of which they are asked.

And then pediatrics has some unexpected and interesting by-products. Only my experience as a pediatrician could have prepared me to solve the mystery of the Mona Lisa smile.

Pediatrics and the Mystery of the Mona Lisa Smile

Last year I made it to the Louvre. I stood dutifully in front of the Mona Lisa, along with other tourists, to gasp the expected "Oohs" and "Aahs." I was particularly interested in her enigmatic smile, a smile whose meaning had eluded clear explanation until now. Suddenly as I was gazing at that smile a buzzer went off in my mind. I had seen that smile before. It was clear as day. There could be no mistake. It came to me in a flash.

For some years I was a camp physician. I used to wander over to the pool to see how the children were making out. I would notice that various of the kids in the shallow end would suddenly stop what they were doing, look around casually or pretend to be casual, hold still for a moment, and then a funny little half-smile would appear on their faces, the same secretive, slightly-off-center smile with the lips just slightly turned up at the edge, that I now saw on the Mona Lisa. It was the smile of relief and secret triumph at bladder release. I can only postulate that Leonardo, who was known as a hard taskmaster, had insisted that his model sit for many hours before him without being allowed up. The pain and urgency must have been unbearable. She probably could not hold back any longer. Just at the moment of release, Leonardo must have caught her expression. I am sure even he did not appreciate the significance.

HOW TO PLAY
TEMPERATURE TAG

To play temperature tag, the following pieces are needed: a sick child, a thermometer, a mother, a telephone, and a doctor. The game begins when the mother puts her hand on the child's head and says, "Boy, it is hot. I'd better take his temperature."

Usually a brief skirmish ensues. The mother says, "Will you keep still, I do not want to hurt you."

At this point the child hears only the word HURT and he struggles even more.

"If you won't sit still, I'll have to call your father."

More struggling. After five minutes, by which time the excessive activity has caused the temperature to rise only one or two degrees, the mother gets the temperature at let us say 103°. Often she says, "Let's see, this is a rectal thermometer, so I subtract one degree, and it is only 102°. It says in my baby book that if my child has more than 101°, I'd better call the doctor."

The harried doctor is dutifully phoned. He usually replies, "Give him some aspirin, and call me back if the temperature goes up."

Thus the game of tag begins. Four hours later, there is a repetition of the first battle scene. It is now 104°, minus one degree discount for rectal insertion. Call the doctor again. He is tied up, he will call you back. Two hours later, the doctor calls back.

"It was 103° two hours ago, Doctor, but he feels cooler now."

"Fine," says the doctor. "Give him some more aspirin and call me back."

This game of tag between mother and doctor, in which the mother is "it" if the temperature goes up and must "tag" the doctor if she can catch him, is a nonsensical game. Its only merit is to increase the value of telephone stocks.

A child with fever usually has an infection of some sort. There are very few exceptions to this rule. The height of the fever is no way to gauge the severity of the illness. It is important to remember the following:

1. Children tend to have a higher temperature when infected than adults.

2. The temperature will fluctuate in the course of the infection. This fluctuation is not an indicator that the child is better or worse.

3. The temperature-taking distracts the mother from more important observations she should make.

4. High fever itself does not cause any damage to the brain, heart, or kidneys. It is the underlying disease that is responsible. Roseola, a common viral disease of infancy and early childhood, causes the highest fever and yet rarely, if ever, has any serious consequences, despite the fact that convulsions may occur.

5. While high fevers may cause convulsions, the majority of these are short and not dangerous. A child having one convulsion due to fever can usually be prevented from having another with the use of some anticonvulsant agent. There are some families in which convulsions may occur at relatively low temperatures, 103°, for example. There are other families in which convulsions due to fever will never occur, not even if the temperature goes up to 106°. There is a hereditary predisposition to convulsion due to fever. About ten per cent of all children have a convulsion at one time or other. Aspirin and sponging with tepid water, alcohol, or alcohol and water can always be used to reduce fever, no matter what the cause.

The important thing we care about is not the temperature but symptoms. Difficulty in breathing may be extremely serious and yet be accompanied by only a slight fever. I can remember several instances when mothers were under-concerned about their children because the low temperature misled them. When I inquired about signs and symptoms, I got a story of difficulty in breathing. In one instance there was severe croup and in other instances pneumonia.

People may joke about doctors saying, "Give him some aspirin, and call me in the morning." This does not reflect lack of concern on the doctor's part. Unless he is a temperature tag player, he usually asks some questions about the child's signs and symptoms. Very often there are none, and the doctor has to wait and see what happens—more on that later, when we discuss viruses.

There is one important exception: a child of less than three months with fever should be regarded as seriously ill until proven otherwise. The reason for this is that, contrary to popular opinion, he has little resistance to many infectious agents. He may have an overwhelming infection and appear deceptively well. For the child three months or older, aspirin and sponging to reduce temperature may really be all that is necessary in the great majority of instances. I often feel that if aspirin had been discovered after cortisone, it would be regarded with as great respect. Simply because it is cheap and easily obtained should in no way take away its usefulness. It is the only way that virus infections, which are by and large the most common infections in children (estimated up to 85 per cent) can be handled. Antibiotics will not help them.

Ask not why the doctor is NOT giving your child an antibiotic, but rather ask WHY HE IS.

DO NOSES RUN
IN YOUR FAMILY?

One of the most common problems facing parents is the child with the runny nose. Since there are relatively few respiratory infections which cannot be treated adequately, parents do not have too much to worry about. But their anxiety is that it might "turn into something." That "something" is usually pneumonia. Actually the ordinary viruses that cause a cold will not turn into anything, except a pain in the neck. A cold is a cold, is a cold, is a cold. . . .

COLDS

There is no scientific evidence that exposure, dampness, inclement weather, or going out without a hat will aggravate a cold. Despite this, I have known families who have been housebound all winter, until it was almost necessary to take one or all of them outside to the nearest mental institution. "What can I do, he is driving me crazy—I cannot stand it any longer," mothers cry. But as soon as they hear the first sniffle, the whole clan gets locked up again.

I might repeat that there is, of course, no cure for the common cold. Treated, it lasts a week; untreated, it lasts seven days. There are no great remedies either. I am sure I will earn the everlasting gratitude of generations of harried physicians if I say that the best thing for a cold is to ignore it. Some nose drops might relieve the child a little bit, but they are not curative.

There are, of course, noses that run in the family. These

are usually of an allergic nature, and since allergy has a hereditary tendency, it is common in certain families.

There is another kind of runny nose. This is the "EVERY TIME I TAKE HIM OUT HE GETS A COLD" nose.

This is usually "vasomotor rhinitis," a condition whose name describes the reaction of the mucous membrane to cold, by the outpouring of a watery secretion on exposure to cold. It is not an infection and many children outgrow it by repeated exposure to the cold.

Rules for a runny nose on a Sunday afternoon:

Try to ignore it.

Send the children out to play. (If other children get it, remember this is a democracy, and we have no rights to exclusivity.)

Actually, at certain times of the year the various viruses causing colds are ubiquitous, and only chance and certain unknown factors determine whether or not we shall get them. The more colds a child is exposed to and gets, the greater the immunity he is likely to develop.

This casual attitude does not apply to infants who, contrary to popular belief, have no resistance to colds. Infants can become very uncomfortable with colds because they do not breathe very easily through their mouths.

If the child is very uncomfortable, put in some nose drops, never more than for about five days since nose drops can make a nose run after that. A cold steam vaporizer might help.

Coughing with a cold: Most parents either forget or do not know that a certain amount of coughing is good. Coughing is a reflex whose purpose is to clear the respiratory tract of mucous. If we did not have this reflex, we might all drown in our own secretions. It follows, therefore, that it is not necessary in most cases to give a cough mixture. If the child is awakened from sleep by coughing, a mixture containing a cough suppressant may be administered.

What not to do for a cold: Do not ask your doctor for antibiotics. Antibiotics in general should be reserved for the complications of a cold, and have no effect on the cold virus itself. Do not fiddle with the diet too much. A fair amount of fluids may be helpful, but not essential. Do not push one kind of food or another on your child. He is miserable enough already. The one possible exception is chicken soup. No doctor in his right mind would ever tell anybody's grandmother that chicken soup is not good for just about everything, from leprosy to the common cold.

ALLERGY

If your child is forever getting a cold, and you have been attributing this to the weather, think of the possibility of allergy, particularly if there is a history of allergy in your family. By that I mean do either you or your husband or any of your sisters or your cousins or your aunts or your parents, have hay fever, eczema, or asthma? If the answer is yes, remember that the potentiality for allergy is inherited, not the specific allergy. If your child is plagued by frequent respiratory infections, you may have to remind your doctor—be gentle—of the possibility of allergy. He may see him only during the acute illness and may need your help in getting the whole picture.

If there is a strong family history of allergy, I would advise against the acquisition of traditional pets like cats and dogs. My rule for the allergic child is, "Man's best friend is the goldfish."

Allergy, when it affects the respiratory tract, can cause not only runny noses but also wheezing, asthma, recurrent bouts of bronchitis, or even in some instances be the underlying cause of some cases of recurrent pneumonia. Recurrent ear infections are also often a result of allergy.

How to Avoid the Allergy Trap

Allergies involving the respiratory tract are likely to be due to inhalants. This is not always the case, however, particularly in younger age groups. For example, chronic runny noses or even wheezing may be the result of milk allergy. But by and large, if the respiratory tract is involved, some inhalant is the most likely cause of the allergic reaction. Commonest among the inhalants is household dust. A well-known pediatrician-allergist told me recently that a great number of the children referred to him are helped by cutting down the amount of dust that the child is exposed to. If you know that your child has respiratory allergies or there is a strong family history of allergy, it might be wise for you to follow the directions I am going to set down, either to help the already affected child or as a preventative.

Admittedly it is difficult to keep the sensitive child in a relatively dust-free environment during the day; however, if we could make his bedroom as dust-free as possible, we would be helping the situation a great deal.

HEATING:

One of the reasons that allergic conditions frequently worsen during the winter months is the heating system. Heating systems, particularly hot air ones, stir up dust. Steam or hot water is preferable to hot air systems. A dust filter, made of several layers of cheesecloth, over the hot air outlets is helpful. The filter should be changed frequently. Cracks or holes around pipes or radiators should be covered.

THE ROOM:

After having checked the heating system, the next step is the preparation of the room. Start from scratch. (Scratching, by the way, may be an allergic manifestation.) Empty the room completely and thoroughly, clean it, remembering to clean and scrub the woodwork to remove all traces of dust. The floor should be waxed.

The room, if possible, should contain only one bed, preferably an iron bed. If box springs are used, there should be a dust-proof casing. The mattress should have a dust-proof cover. Do not use a mattress pad. Fuzzy wool blankets or feather- or wool-stuffed comforters should not be used. There are many adequate blankets or quilts made out of synthetics, such as dacron, which are excellent.

Plain, non-upholstered chairs made of wood or metal are best. I once saw a child whose asthma was markedly improved when an overstuffed easy chair was removed from his bedroom.

The room should be cleaned and aired daily, after which it should be kept shut.

Clothing, particularly woolens, should be kept in another room. All animals with fur or feathers should be kept out of the room.

Needless to say the remainder of the house should be

kept as dust-free as possible. In general it is best to keep the house well humidified. Dryness seems to increase the likelihood of infections, which may trigger off allergies, and in addition moisture tends to keep down dust.

After you have done all this, your child may get a better night's sleep. If he doesn't, you certainly will. You will be exhausted.

As I have stated previously, most runny noses and allergies of the respiratory tract such as asthma are caused by inhalants. It has been reported, however, that an approach to the allergic problem on a dietary basis could have far-reaching beneficial effects on children who have a tendency toward asthma and eczema. When one considers that thirty per cent of the chronic health problems of American children are allergic in origin it is easy to see why any hints on preventing the allergy trap are important.

In 1953 Drs. Johnston and Glazer of Rochester, New York, showed that a preventative diet used from infancy for children whose families were plagued by allergies could have a significant effect in preventing major respiratory allergies and eczema. This study when repeated later by Dr. Johnston seemed to confirm the earlier findings. What he suggests, and it is a regime I would recommend, is placing infants from highly allergic families on a restricted diet, in which cow's milk, beef, egg, and wheat are withheld from the diet from birth to from six to nine months of age. Dr. Johnston's studies indicate that this could mean that the child from a highly allergic family would have a seventy-five per cent less chance of developing allergic runny nose, asthma, or eczema.

It is such a simple thing to do that one wonders why it is not done more often. Soybean milk preparations are plentiful and cheap. Wheat is not an essential part of a diet, and there are many non-wheat cereals. Lamb is a highly nutritious meat, a good source of protein, and can be used as a substitute for beef products.

I am very hopeful that dust-proofing children's rooms and the allergic preventative diet, though requiring effort and patience on the mother's part, may help cut down that thirty per cent figure of chronic allergic illness that bedevils the American parent.

HOW TO AVOID
PENICILLIN SHOTS,
OR WHAT IS A VIRUS?

A patient once called her doctor angrily. "Doctor, I thought you said I had a 24-hour virus. How come I have been sick for two days now?"

"Well," replied the doctor, "you probably have two 24-hour viruses back to back."

Why does your doctor keep saying, "You've got a virus"? It is difficult to make a diagnosis of a specific virus, but a general diagnosis is relatively easy. Viruses are by far the most common infectious agents. As I mentioned previously, it has been estimated that up to 85 per cent of all infections are caused by viruses. As of this writing there are no antibiotics that are effective against them (the trachoma virus, which does not occur in this part of the world, may be the only exception).

Practically all upper-respiratory infections are caused by viruses, and most gastrointestinal infections are caused by viruses. These are the two most common infections in infants.

WHAT IS A VIRUS ANYWAY?

A virus is a small particle measuring in size from two to one hundred millimicrons—or about 1/100 of the size of bacteria—and is composed of one or two types of nucleic acid: desoxyribonucleic acid or ribonucleic acid.

Viruses live within cells, in contrast to bacteria which live outside of cells. Since they live within cells, they are usually late in producing outward manifestations or signs. For example, you may feel vaguely ill for a week or two before you get yellow or jaundiced and your doctor can diagnose hepatitis. More commonly in children there may be a high fever for three days before a rash appears and roseola can be diagnosed. Too, because viruses live within cells, it will be hard to develop an effective agent to attack them without disrupting cells of the body.

Let us get back to how to avoid penicillin shots and other antibiotics, which may be the most important advice I have for mothers on the subject of viruses.

The story is told, and unfortunately it probably is not aprocryphal, about a doctor who admitted a patient to a hospital. He told the nurse to give the patient 600,000 units of penicillin intramuscularly for three days. "If he is not better in three days," he told the nurse, "I'll come in and examine him." Damn nice of you, Jack.

Parents are partly to blame for the overuse of antibiotics. One way to raise my blood pressure is to have someone phone me and say, "Doc, my child has a cold; I want you to give him a shot of penicillin."

There are three errors committed in the seemingly simple request. First, and leastly, do not call me "Doc." Doc is what you call a football trainer.

Secondly, a cold, by definition, is a viral infection and will not respond to penicillin.

Third, do not expect a self-respecting physician to respond to a summons to dispense a parental prescription.

During a recent house visit, my examination of a nine-year-old boy with a temperature of 103° revealed nothing. This is often the case when viruses are involved. I explained the situation to his family rather carefully, I thought, and recommended that the little boy be given aspirin. His father, a big bellowy man, looked displeased. "Doc," he said, "I want you to give him some medicine with active ingredients."

This huge consumer father, upon whose smooth cerebrum the entire advertising industry was focusing its beams, had gotten the message: "Something with active ingredients." Needless to say, it would be almost impossible to engage that father in any sophisticated discussion of viruses. He could not understand, not at the present time, that there is no effective medication against them. Nor could he understand that the administration of an antibiotic could do more harm than good. If indeed it was a virus infection, antibiotics, rather than protecting the child from secondary infections, could have made him more prone to infections that resist antibiotics.

Let us say that my impression that this was a virus was mistaken. He may have been starting with an infection of some other kind which the antibiotic might mask. It is not professional pride that makes good doctors insist on making a proper diagnosis before treatment; rather it is their desire to treat rationally and to make an accurate determination of the sites of infection.

A most outstanding example is a urinary tract infection. This is an infection involving the plumbing system, comprised of the kidney, the ureters, the bladder, and the urethra. It may occur without any symptoms at all. The only way it may be accurately diagnosed is by urine examination. Many ordinary antibiotics are likely to be effective against bacteria that commonly cause urinary tract infection; therefore a doctor might seemingly cure a child of a urinary tract infection without knowing it. The fact that the child is having a urinary tract infection is important to know. It may indicate some blockage in the plumbing system, which, if discovered and corrected, could save the vital kidneys from irreparable damage.

Lastly, antibiotics, all antibiotics, have side effects. There is no sense risking these without good scientific justification. The old motto, *"Premum non nocere,"* "In the first place, do no harm," should be remembered by parents and doctors alike.

WHAT THE HECK
ARE THOSE LUMPS?

"Honey," your husband intones somewhat menacingly, "will you come here? Jennifer looks like a squirrel hoarding acorns in her mouth."

Sure enough, she does look like a fat-cheeked squirrel. You look more closely. It is Jennifer all right. She has a swelling just behind her ear extending down over the jawbone. The swelling is usually not red, may not be very tender, and, if she will let you touch it, has a gelatinous feel. I mention the feel of it because swollen lymph nodes usually have a firm feel. In addition, lymph nodes usually occur lower down on the neck. If your child was exposed to mumps two or three weeks before and now has the swelling I have described, it is reasonable to assume she has the mumps.

MUMPS

Mumps usually start on one side and then several days later can affect the other side. The signs and symptoms accompanying it are variable. There may or may not be fever (that's a help, isn't it). Headaches and abdominal pain are quite common. Should either of these occur, I suggest that you contact your doctor. There is nothing alarming about either of these symptoms, but he may want to know. A headache may indicate mumps involvement of the nervous system. Mumps encephalitis is surprisingly common, and the patient almost always recovers promptly without after-effects, this despite the ominous sounding "encephalitis." The second symptom, abdominal pain with or without vomiting, is uncomfortable but not serious.

Jennifer with the mumps would have no problem, but Jeffrey, if he were at adolescence or beyond, might get involvement of his testicles. One testicle is usually involved, but both may be. Mumps, even when it occurs in both testicles, rarely causes sterility. However, since it can and since mumps is usually so mild in children, I would suggest, as do many medical authorities, the deliberate exposure of a boy to mumps before he reaches puberty.

It is a common misconception, held even by doctors, that mumps on only one side does not confer immunity. The likelihood is that mumps occurring on one or both sides confers lifelong immunity.

There are children who have been known to get recurrent swelling of the parotid or salivary gland, which also happens in the case of mumps. This may be because of sensitivity or allergy. I once cured a boy who had had three bouts of "mumps" by taking him off pickles.

Being a doctor is not so easy, is it? For that matter, neither is being a parent.

Treatment: Actually there is no specific treatment for mumps. The swelling might enlarge rapidly, causing pain. A wet compress may be helpful. I usually prefer a cool compress, but my grandmother preferred a warm one. I really do not know which is best.

Aspirin for the relief of pain or fever is helpful. Occasionally pain can be brought on by eating or drinking something tart or bitter, such as citrus juice or spices; so you may want to avoid these. A child with mumps need not be kept in bed unless he is sick enough to want to stay there himself. A child with mumps is contagious until the swelling is gone. This usually takes a week to ten days.

Good luck.

SWOLLEN GLANDS

Swollen glands aren't swollen glands at all, technically. Rather they are swollen lymph nodes. Glands are organs that secrete a hormone. The so-called glands that usually swell in the neck do not secrete anything but consist of lymph tissue which acts as a barrier against infection.

As I have already mentioned, swollen lymph nodes are most often confused with mumps. Sometimes it is difficult even for a doctor to distinguish between the two.

Swollen lymph nodes usually are the result of a throat infection or any infection in the upper respiratory passages. They may be present on one or both sides. They are often associated with fever but need not be so. They may vary in size from marbles to plums. They usually are tender, and sometimes the skin around them looks red, which is usually not the case in mumps. They are situated in the neck, well below the angle of the jaw, and have a firm feel, all in contrast to the usual case of mumps.

Swollen glands are most often the result of a bacterial infection which can be treated by antibiotics. That is why, among other reasons, it is important to distinguish them from mumps.

Viruses can also cause the swelling of the lymph nodes. The Coxackie virus, the adeno virus, and the virus or viruses associated with infectious mononucleosis do this. Therefore your doctor may want to do a blood count if the swollen glands do not respond to treatment or he is in doubt about the diagnosis.

Cat scratch fever can also cause swelling of the lymph nodes. The swelling in the lymph nodes—notice I am not saying gland any longer—follows by one to three weeks the appearance of inflammation or the development of a small bump or papule at the site of the scratch. There is no specific treatment for this, but fortunately it is not dangerous.

Swollen lymph nodes may occur in sites other than the neck. There are also nodes in the armpits, on the inner side of the elbow, and in the groin. As I have mentioned, they act as barriers to infection. An infection of the knee may cause nodes in the groin to swell just as an infection in the throat or tonsils will cause nodes in the neck to swell. A cat scratch on the arm may cause swelling of the nodes in the armpit.

If all of this seems a bit confusing, just remember one rule: if you don't know what the hell the lump is, don't just stand there and worry—consult your doctor.

WHAT THE HECK
ARE THOSE SPOTS?

Sometimes when you are dressing or undressing your child you will notice some spots. If you are like most parents, your first reaction will be, "What the heck are those spots?" Children seem to break out in spots just before their parents are planning a holiday.

The easiest way to think of what it might be is to divide spots into two groups. The first group we will call:

SPOTS WITHOUT WARNING

In this group the spots will usually appear unheralded by any indication that the child is really sick.

Chicken Pox

The most common cause of sudden spots is chicken pox. Usually chicken pox occurs 11 to 21 days after exposure. The trouble is that chicken pox is so darned contagious that your child can pick it up simply by passing someone with it in the supermarket; hence you may not even suspect that he has been exposed. What also is not commonly known is that children can pick up chicken pox from someone with shingles. The reverse is also true. Elderly people in particular can pick up shingles from children. So keep Granny away if the kids have chicken pox.

It is true that children coming down with chicken pox can be out of sorts or may even have low grade fevers, but usually this goes unnoticed. The rash you will first see is made up of small crops of small red bumps on a red base. The color scheme is quite arbitrary. These crops come out for three to four days, during which time the child may run a slight fever. These small bumps are usually about the size of a millet seed. What begins as a millet seed may turn into something that looks like a tear drop. Soon crusts will form on all the bumps.

Pox may involve the mouth or throat and account for the complaint of a sore throat. The pox may also involve the vagina in girls.

There isn't a "chicken" in every pox. There are a whole lot of poxes recently described that look a little like chicken pox. Some of these are caused by the Echo virus. Echo, by the way, does not mean that it keeps coming back. It is an acronym (an acronym is a word formed from the first letter of several words—it is not a disease) for Enteric Cytopathogenic Human Orphan Strain. Try that on your doctor for laughs.

These pox are usually fewer in number, usually occur in the summer, and do not scab as readily. From the practical point of view it does not make much difference since neither is serious.

What to do for chicken pox: In most instances, a doctor need not see a child with chicken pox. I can see no reason why a child should stay in bed. Usually he won't want to. A bath once or twice a day with an antiseptic soap is good. It makes him feel more comfortable and will prevent infection. I have found that a cool bath is better than a hot bath because it helps reduce fever if there is any and hot water intensifies itching. A little cornstarch added to the bath, enough to make it cloudy, may also reduce itching. Calamine lotion, that old standby, should be applied several times a day. An antihistamine, the drug used for allergies such as hay fever, may be needed if the itching is very intense.

When can I let the child out of the house? He is driving me mad. The crusts will last for about two weeks, but do not panic. You can let him out seven days after the appearance of the rash, at which time he is no longer contagious.

People do not carry chicken pox. I mean by that that it is all right for you or your other children to go out and visit. It is all right to have a baby-sitter, if she has had chicken pox. It would be extremely unlikely that she could bring it home and affect her household.

Did I get you out of a spot there?

Chicken pox is usually benign. However, it can be, notice I said "can be," serious in a child who is taking some form of cortisone. In that case, if you know your child has been exposed, let your doctor know.

German Measles

The only thing that measles and German measles have in common is the name. They are distinct viruses. German measles is by far the milder of the two diseases. This is surprising, considering the reputation of the Germans.

Again, these spots can occur without warning. There may be a slight fever accompanying the rash or there may be no symptoms at all. In German measles there are spots and bumps. The spots are usually distinct blotches which, as they fade, run together like a Jackson Pollock painting. More characteristic than the rash are the bumps. Bumps that are actually swollen lymph nodes appear at the base of the skull, behind the ears, and in the back of the neck. They usually are quite prominent and may be tender. The whole business is over in three to four days. I can see no reason to keep a child in bed for this. German measles is usually mild. During the last epidemic, I noted that swelling of the hands and fingers occurred in adults, but I do not remember seeing it in a child.

The greatest danger from German measles is to a fetus under three months of age. Therefore, keep recently impregnated ladies who have not had German measles clear of your house. If a woman in the first twelve weeks of pregnancy should be exposed, she ought to contact a physician.

Of course, there are other spots, such as insect bites, or allergies, that may conceivably confuse you. I am not trying to make a doctor out of anybody. If you find a rash confusing, show it to your doctor. He may find it confusing too.

SPOTS WITH WARNING

The spots we are now going to deal with usually occur in a child who has been ill for a couple of days.

Measles, Alias Red or Day Measles, or the Bad Kind.

A child who is going to break out in the rash of measles will be sick with fever and a cough for three to four days before the appearance of the rash. I have seen children sick for a week before the rash appears, which is kind of a strain on the patient, the parents, and the pediatrician. There is an old wives' tale floating about that you can make the measles "come out" by giving the child hot baths. The only thing that "comes out" is dirt: save your strength.

Two days or so before the rash shows up, little white spots may appear on the inside of the cheek. These spots resemble flecks of oatmeal except that they cannot be washed away.

The spots of measles first appear behind the ears and on the neck and at the hairline. They are, at first, dark red spots, which spread downward. At first also, they are distinct, and then they run together. There may be swelling of the face.

A child with measles should be seen by a doctor. While there is no specific treatment for the disease, you need a doctor to be on the alert for complications.

Measles is serious enough but its reputation for destructiveness goes beyond the facts. Contrary to popular view, ordinary measles does not damage the eyes, weaken the kidneys, nor impair the hearing. There may be ear infections, bronchitis, or pneumonia. Fortunately these complications, when they occur, can be handled by antibiotics despite the fact that they cannot always be prevented by them. Your doctor will decide, often depending on the age of the child, whether the administration of an antibiotic before complications set in is indicated.

There is no longer any need for any child to get measles. There are two vaccines available to give immunity against measles, and gamma globulin either to prevent it or modify it, if you know within five days or so that the child has been exposed. Naturally we prefer the vaccines, to avoid running any risks. By the way, what does not seem to be generally known is that about one child in every 1000 with measles gets encephalitis. It only has to happen to you once, so get your child immunized.

Measles is contagious until the fever is gone and the rash has faded.

Scarlet Fever

The child who is going to get the rash of scarlet fever will be sick from one day to as long as three days in advance, rarely longer. He will usually have a fever and a sore throat. He may appear mildly to severely ill. The rash usually appears on the neck, the chest, and in the armpits. A short time later it appears in the groin. The rash then appears as a blush over the entire body. Because the hair follicles swell, the rash has a sandpapery feel. The face is usually spared, although there may be a pallor around the mouth. The tongue may become quite red on the edges, and if the body of it is white, it gets the appearance of the so-called strawberry tongue.

How to treat scarlet fever: Most physicians agree that in the last twenty years, for reasons unknown, scarlet fever has become a milder disease. Generally, if you tell parents that their child has scarlet fever, they panic. Scarlet fever is nothing more nor less than a strep throat and a rash. Now you would not panic if I said your child had a strep throat, would you? Maybe you would. We parents are something, aren't we?

Now a strep throat should be taken seriously, but it is not critical. As of this writing there are no streptococci, that is the germ that causes strep throat, that can resist penicillin. A child with a strep infection should be treated for ten days with penicillin to prevent rheumatic fever. It is also effective in cutting down on the chance of nephritis (kidney inflammation). Both of these may occur after a strep throat. If your child is sensitive to penicillin, your physician will ordinarily choose another antibiotic to use. Let your doctor follow the child to detect complications should they arise.

Roseola Infantum

Roseola is an infection that many infants get. It occurs most often between six months and two years, but may occur a little earlier or a little later. In the vast majority of cases, it starts suddenly with a high fever. "He didn't act sick, but I put my hand on his head. He was burning up. I took his temperature and it was 104°." This is a typical way that this illness is first reported to the doctor. Rarely, the first symptom is a convulsion. Fortunately the convulsion is usually short. The fever usually lasts 72 hours, the temperature rising and falling during the course of the day. Through it all the child's condition seems to belie the height of the temperature. He is often in good spirits, sometimes hungry, particularly after aspirin. Occasional mild cold symptoms will accompany the illness. Glands in the back of the neck or behind the ears or head can sometimes be felt. Roseola is probably a virus disease; in any event it is unaffected by antibiotics. After 72 hours the temperature will drop and a faint, sometimes fleeting, rash, red and flat or sometimes slightly raised, will appear, mostly on the trunk. When the rash appears, the baby is better. It is a frightening experience the first time, but fortunately complications are extremely rare.

WHEN CHILDREN
SHOULD BE SHOT

All children in the United States should be immunized against diphtheria, tetanus, whooping cough, poliomyelitis, measles, and smallpox. Most American doctors have never seen children with diphtheria, tetanus, or small pox. This is a tribute to the efficacy of mass immunizations rather than a lack of clinical experience. Polio is becoming happily rare, and it is my devout hope some day to have to describe the disease to new generations of doctors who will never have seen it.

One word of warning about measles: many people regard measles as benign and feel that "every kid has to get it sometime." Actually, measles has accounted for more mortality and morbidity than polio ever did, but it didn't have the right press agents. Fortunately there are two vaccines available to prevent this disease. Since one out of one thousand with measles may get encephalitis, I urge you to have your child immunized.

Here is a suggested guide to immunizations which agrees generally with the current recommendations of the Committee in Control of Infectious Diseases of the American Academy of Pediatrics. It is, of course, subject to modifications.

Two months—diphtheria, tetanus, pertussis (whooping cough), called DPT; oral polio vaccine, known hereafter as OPV

Three months—DPT, OPV

Four months—DPT, OPV

Nine months—a tuberculin test administered by your

doctor to see whether the child has been exposed to tuberculosis.

Twelve months—measles vaccine. Your doctor will know whether the live or killed measles vaccine is indicated.

Fifteen months—smallpox vaccine, DPT, OPV

Two years—tuberculin test

Three years—tuberculin test

Four years—DPT, tuberculin test

Six years—smallpox vaccine, tuberculin test, OPV

Eight years—DT (pertussis vaccine is no longer recommended)

Twelve years—DT

Sixteen years—DT

N.B. Most doctors will continue to do yearly tuberculin tests. Tetanus boosters should be continued at regular intervals of three or four years throughout life.

I suggest that you keep your own record of your children's shots since people move around so much, and there is always a possibility that an official record will be lost.

ABOUT THE
ALIMENTARY TRACT

NAUSEA AND VOMITING

Nausea and vomiting can be brought on in children by a wide variety of causes. Infections in or out of the intestinal tract, overeating, sometimes some emotional factors, are all common causes of nausea and its sequel, vomiting.

No matter what the cause of nausea or vomiting, you can do the following. Stop all feeding for at least one hour. If your child seems thirsty, you may moisten his lips or offer him some ice chips. Remember the first thing to do is rest his intestinal tract, either by no feeding or underfeeding.

After one hour—it probably will seem like ten—you may give him one teaspoonful of any carbonated beverage. It need not be warm. For some reason or other, children seem to tolerate carbonated beverages better than plain fruits. If this is not available, tap water will do.

Repeat the teaspoonful offering every fifteen minutes three or four times. If he tolerates that, you may want to increase it to two ounces. If there is any vomiting, go back one step. A moistened lollipop is helpful to soothe the child and as a source of energy.

If there is no further vomiting, you can then increase the fluids; add apple or grape juice to the regime, then move on to soups and crackers and later weak tea and toast.

If your child insists on milk, as many do, you can offer half water, half skim milk. I try to keep whole milk and other fatty foods, such as eggs, meats, cheeses and butter, away from the child who is vomiting. I guess a little butter on toast will not hurt. Go ahead—I am not looking. If he tolerates all this, you are more or less on your own. Play it by ear, and add a few new foods as he seems to want them, saving on fatty foods for last. In two or three days he should be back to his regular diet, following a bout with vomiting.

If the child who has been vomiting also has acute abdominal pain, there is a danger of appendicitis. See page 171.

DIARRHEA

Diarrhea, by definition, is the presence of an increased number of watery stools. Diarrhea, like its upstairs neighbor, can also be caused by any infection in or out of the intestinal tract, dietary indiscretions, or sometimes emotions. I doubt that a change in the water or in the brand of milk causes it, but I am sure I will get plenty of disagreement. The principle of treating diarrhea is the same as that for treating vomiting—resting the intestinal tract.

1. *Stop milk.* A well-known pediatrician with more than half a century of practice states that he has never had to hospitalize a child for treatment of acute diarrhea because as soon as it starts, he recommends the immediate removal of milk. It certainly is an extremely effective thing to do.

2. *Fluid replacement.* I know of no word more likely to conjure up fear in mothers of infants than diarrhea. I think there is an exaggerated fear of diarrhea, because it is misunderstood. The diarrhea per se is not the problem. The problem arises only if *because* of the diarrhea the child puts out more fluid and salts in his watery bowel movements than he takes in. When a child loses more fluids than he takes in, he gets dry or "dehydrated." The first thing that may happen is that he will stop urinating because his kidneys are trying to conserve fluids.

To replace lost fluids and salt, I suggest the following solution:

> One quart of water
> One-third teaspoon of salt
> One tablespoon of sugar

Notice, I added only one-third teaspoon of salt to the quart of water. It is better to be over-conservative because too much salt may be harmful. This solution can be given to a child of any age.

Apple juice may also be offered. It is palatable, contains the essential salts, and has a binding agent in it, pectin. If the diarrhea is not too severe, I have no objection to offering half water and half skim milk. By not too severe, I mean the child is not stooling every hour or so. I think that whole skim milk should be avoided in infants with moderate to severe diarrhea. It can result in hypernatremia. Ask your doctor about that one. In the meantime, do as I say first.

As the child gets better, banana, scraped raw apple, rice or rice cereal, carrots, or lean meats may be offered if the child is hungry. I do not recommend strong tea for a moderate to severe diarrhea because tea is a diuretic—that is, an agent that increases urination. This might result in further fluid loss.

Absorbents that help bind the stool may be used. They are not particularly important in the treatment of diarrhea save as they may make the child feel a little more comfortable. They are not relevant to the major problem, which is fluid replacement. Kaopectate, one or two teaspoons depending on the age of the infant, may be given.

The above recommendations may be followed until you can get in contact with the doctor or in cases where the diarrhea seems mild and is abating. If the diarrhea persists, or the child seems dry, get in touch with your physician.

VOMITING AND DIARRHEA

If vomiting and diarrhea occur together, stop all feedings for one hour, and then start with the salt solution described on page 143.

CAN UNDESCENDED TESTICLES CAUSE CONSTIPATION, OR HOW ONE THING DOES NOT LEAD TO ANOTHER

═══════════════════

One morning during my telephone hour an anonymous voice asked, "Can undescended testicles cause constipation?" Frankly I had not given the matter much thought. I don't mean that I haven't concerned myself with undescended testicles, nor that I had never contemplated the problem of constipation; I just hadn't thought of them together.

With years of experience in answering unprecedented questions and strong motivation not to offend my anonymous questioner, I replied that although it was unlikely, nevertheless it was possible. I could not, of course, see any anatomical connection between the two conditions, but possibly the relationship might be psychological. (This is in keeping with the modern medical tradition of attributing emotional causes to symptoms for which you can find no other reason.) I stated that if her boy—I assumed it was a boy—otherwise we would have a different category of problem—was to become aware of his undescended testicles, this might cause him to have castration anxiety, which in turn could cause him to regress to a more infantile state of libidinal development, which in turn could cause him to hold back on his stools, which in turn would constipate him. Are you dizzy from all those turns?

Actually the two problems are unrelated. Undescended

145

testicles are fairly common. It is perfectly possible to be normally reproductive with only one testicle descended. A boy with neither testicle descended will have all the secondary sexual characteristics of a normal male, which he will be, but he won't produce sperm for reproduction.

It is for this reason that if both testicles are undescended, an early operation, about the age of five, is advocated to increase the chances of the development of a testes that can produce sperm.

If one testicle is descended, the matter is not nearly so urgent. It is advisable, nevertheless, to try to bring the other testicle down.

The process by which the testicles descend from an area near the kidneys where they have formed downward into the scrotum has been referred to as "the fall of man." Notwithstanding any poetic allusions, the problem is anatomical and the solution is surgical. Different physicians advocate different ages for the operation, but all agree that if it is to be done, it is far better done before puberty.

CONSTIPATION

Having dispatched with the problem of undescended testicles, I am left with the problem of constipation. Rather, my patient is.

In most instances of constipation there are no anatomic causes. There are rare infants who have alterations in their bowel patterns from birth—usually severe constipation—who do have an anatomical defect known as Hirschprungs disease. This is a narrowing of the rectum due to the absence of small nerves connected to the involuntary nervous system. These children, as do others with an anatomical cause of obstruction, require surgery.

The anatomical causes of constipation are very rare indeed. One must *not* conclude, however, that if no anatomical problem is found the cause of constipation is necessarily psychological. There are doctors who say, in reference to constipation, that it is not a question of what the child is eating, but rather what's eating the child. I sometimes wonder what's eating the doctors. While not denying the occasional presence of emotional causes, I should think it would be helpful to the already over-psychologized parent to hear about other factors.

Dr. Murray Davidson, an outstanding pediatric gastroenterologist, stresses the fact that constipation tends to be hereditary and that the muscular mobility pattern of the rectum of constipated children differs somewhat from that of non-constipated children. He also points out that milk, because of its low roughage content and high calcium content, tends to be constipating. Infants and children tend to take in large amounts of milk, thus aggravating any already existing tendency to constipation.

Stool holding: Although many doctors emphasize the psychological aspects of stool holding, Dr. Davidson, while neither denying nor affirming emotions as causality, explains how physiology may be the reason for the mildly constipated child becoming a stool holder. The same muscles, mainly the diaphragm and the muscles of the abdomen, are used both in voluntary defecation and holding back. The only difference in the two actions rests on leverage. In most instances, to have a voluntary bowel movement, the feet must push against a firm surface. This explains why many children when placed on a high commode cannot have a bowel movement, but when taken off the seat will squat in a corner and have one. It's not more love they need, it's more leverage.

It is also true that a constipated child with a large hard stool will find it painful to defecate. This will further exaggerate his tendency to hold back because of fear of pain. This in turn causes his mother or father to lose patience with him, and thus secondary rather than primary emotional factors develop. I do not doubt that there are some children who reflect their emotional disturbance in either constipation or stool holding, but I am trying to strike a balance, without, of course, under any circumstance striking the child.

Paradoxically, the problems of constipation can lead to fecal soiling or, as it is known in the trade, "encopresis." In this situation the child will unconsciously or consciously soil himself. Here again a knowledge of physiology will help clarify the problem. As the child holds back, his rectum becomes filled with stool. A large enough mass in the rectum will so stretch it that the signals to defecate which the child normally feels will be diminished. In addition, the water-absorbing capacity of the rectum will be impaired and as a result watery stool will begin to leak out of the rectum. Thus the child may seem to be having too frequent bowel movements, when in reality his basic problem is constipation.

How do we clear up the whole mess? The first approach to constipation, stool holding, or fecal soiling should rest on physiological rather than psychological principles. In other words, visit your druggist before you visit the psychiatrist.

1. Evacuate the rectum, the seat of our problems. If the child hasn't had a bowel movement in several days, there

is probably a large amount of bulky feces in his rectum which will have to be removed by enema. A hypertonic phosphate solution, already prepared for insertion, is available at your druggist's. About one ounce of this solution should be used for every 20 pounds of the child's weight, with a maximum of four ounces given in pairs, the second enema to follow the first by about an hour. Usually three or four pairs of enemas given in the morning and at night are sufficient to clear out the stool. Never use plain water for enemas.

2. After enemas are given, or even if they are not required (your child has only been constipated for 24 hours and isn't trying to force out a stool), the next stage consists of the administration of large amounts of mineral oil to establish a good bowel pattern and to prevent the possibility of a painful bowel movement. This may require doses of two to three tablespoons of mineral oil, sometimes even more, to insure a daily, painless bowel movement. Harmful effects from large doses of mineral oil are unlikely. The administration of water soluble multivitamins is recommended for children on such a regime to supplement the vitamins in the diet that may be passed out with the mineral oil and thus not absorbed. Mineral oil is continued for at least a month.

3. The third step in the treatment is regulation of the diet. These changes in the diet should be instituted at the start. First reduce milk intake. As I have previously stated, a pint of milk a day is adequate, and excessive milk is constipating. If necessary, if the child insists on more, the milk may be diluted with up to equal parts of water. The intake of apples, bananas, and pears should be reduced. Increase wheat products; peaches, prunes, berries, melons, and figs are helpful. In children under two years of age, mineral oil may have to be reintroduced from time to time.

In children over two, if attempts have not been made previously, this is a good time to start toilet-training. It should be done in a leisurely, relaxed manner. Remember, however, the rule I mentioned earlier. Bowel movements are not worth fighting over.

TO BED
OR NOT TO BED

I hope I am not disappointing any of my readers by stating right off that this chapter is not a guide to selective promiscuity. I shall leave that sort of advice for your analyst to worry over. I've got enough problems of my own.

I should like to deal with the tendency on the part of many parents and doctors, too, to insist that a child be kept "quiet" in bed when he has any illness. Mothers will usually ask the doctor whether the child can get out of bed. A more proper question is, Why does he have to be in bed in the first place? In most instances, keeping children quiet in bed is a joke anyway. I have seen bedridden children with colds jumping up and down, using the bed as a sort of trampoline. They would have been better off allowed up, perhaps playing with toys or watching T.V. in the living room.

I can think of very few illnesses where keeping a child in bed is mandatory. In most instances, if a child feels well enough to get up, despite his temperature or his cough, he should be permitted to do so. The child is probably the best guide to whether he can be out of bed or not. My statement holds for the vast majority of upper respiratory illnesses such as colds, sinus infections, and ear infections, and lower respiratory infections including bronchitis or pneumonia. You read me right. I said pneumonia. In most cases of bacterial pneumonia, the child initially will want to stay in bed, but after a day or two of the appropriate antibiotic he will feel well enough to be up and about a bit. There is no evidence that exposure or drafts or moving about will increase complications. As for virus pneumonias in children, they are usually so mild that bed rest is unnecessary.

A reasonably contented child rather than a child imprisoned in his bed is likely to get well sooner.

Children with chicken pox, mumps, or measles need not necessarily be kept in bed either if they feel well enough to be up for a bit.

There are, of course, exceptions to my rule of letting the child be the guide. In rheumatic fever, hepatitis, or nephritis, a child may have a sense of well-being and may insist on being active, but in the present state of our knowledge it appears that he should be kept in bed until the acute stage is over. These illnesses are long-term affairs, and liberal use of games, T.V., and reading will help make the experience bearable. In certain instances, your doctor may prescribe sedation to cut down the child's desire for activity.

By way of recapitulation, ask not whether he may get out of bed; ask why he has to be there in the first place.

HOW TO TELL WHETHER
YOUR CHILD IS HOME
FROM SCHOOL SICK—
OR HOMESICK FROM SCHOOL

Every fall I begin to see in my practice a fair number of children with vague abdominal pain. It is very important, obviously, to decide as soon as possible whether this pain is organic or emotional. A diary kept by the parent can be of great value in such a situation. Let me give you a typical example so that you can see how it works.

Not long ago a mother asked me to see her eight-year-old boy. She stated that for several weeks he had had severe abdominal pain and vomiting. There are a wide variety of disorders that can produce these symptoms. Obviously, the gastrointestinal tract might be suspected, less obviously the urinary tract or even the central nervous system, not to mention a great many other possibilities. I asked this mother when the symptoms first appeared. "In the fall," she said. "Was he fine all summer?" I asked. "Oh yes," was her reply, "he had a wonderful summer." "When was he most likely to get the pain?" I asked. "Usually in the morning," she replied, "and he vomits too. It is so bad sometimes that he cannot go to school. Even when he goes, the school nurse has to send him home."

My examination revealed nothing. I did a few simple tests and asked the mother to keep a diary of his episodes and return in ten days. On her return, she reported that he had had the pain through Friday, but during the weekend he did not complain once. Well there it was—crystal clear. There are no organic diseases that take Saturday and Sunday off. A little further investigation revealed that he was a very conscientious boy, a marked contrast to the hooky player, who does not complain and does not go to school either. I found in this particular case that the boy was having trouble in math. This worried him a great deal. He became frightened about school. His anxiety caused him to have pain and to vomit. A little talk with his teacher and some tutoring, and his abdominal pain disappeared. He no longer stays home sick from school.

I have a feeling that we are seeing more so-called school phobias than we used to. The child whose fear of school manifests itself in abdominal pain or nausea—these are the usual signs—is becoming quite common. He or she is usually an excellent student, strongly desirous of doing well—in contrast to the kid who plays truant but pretends he is going to school. The latter leaves quite cheerfully, books in arms, never shows up in school, and spends the afternoon at the movies. The child with school phobia is another kettle of fish. He makes an honest effort to go. Anxiety gets the better of him. The prospect of going to school, of facing trials and possible failures, is too much. He channels his anxiety into health problems. He may experience real pain or true nausea as a result of fear. Finally he gives in, sometimes with the aid of an over-sympathetic mother, and he stays out. Once out of school for a couple of days, it is hard to get him back.

Such a problem needs fairly immediate attention. Your doctor will want to make a few tests to eliminate organic disease and will ask for your observations. He probably will make every effort to get you to get the child back to school. You may resist. You may not be able to separate yourself from your child. Go against your feelings. It is best for you and the child. Be firm.

I might add as a sort of consolation that these problems are more common and will increase as the academic demands on children increase. It is not unusual anymore to see an eleven- or twelve-year-old student faced with two or three hours of homework after a busy day at school. It is paradoxical that in an affluent society, the demands on children are greater than ever. Where are the blessings of the scientific revolution?

WHEN TO CALL
THE PSYCHIATRIST

A psychiatrist is a physician who diagnoses and treats mental illness. This begs the question, of course, because we do not have a clear formulation of what mental illness is.

There is no question but that a child whose abnormal behavior is due to some physical abnormality involving the nervous system is ill. A child with lead poisoning, certain forms of convulsive disorders, disturbances in metabolism —such as low blood sugar (hypoglycemia)—or pressure on the brain from various causes may exhibit personality and behavioral changes as the major, or even only, manifestation of his disorder.

In addition, involvement of organs outside the nervous system may cause difficulties of the same type. The child who does not see or hear well may have school difficulties. A child with hypothyroidism may appear dull and lacking in initiative. The child with anemia or chronic infection may be tired or irritable.

I have not made all these references to organic diseases to scare you. I have done this because I feel that a child with any sort of "psychological difficulty" should have a thorough medical check-up. A careful history, physical examination, and relevant laboratory tests may be extremely helpful. One case sticks out in my mind.

I recently saw a seven-year-old whose difficulties were judged to be emotional. She seemed to daydream a good deal and made funny licking movements with her tongue. It was thought at first that she was disturbed, that her daydreaming was a withdrawal response to the realities of a difficult school situation. In addition she had sleep difficulties and "scary dreams." To further round out the false picture, her father was described as very nervous. She underwent psychotherapy for about nine months.

The mother's dissatisfaction with the diagnosis and treatment made her seek medical aid elsewhere. Examination and tests revealed that this child had a not uncommon type of convulsive disorder, called petit mal. Appropriate drug therapy stopped the "daydreaming" and the "tics" and even many of the secondary psychological disturbances. A thorough physical examination and appraisal for a child who seems to be having behavior difficulties is of prime importance.

Where there is no detectable organic disease, I myself have found that the concept of "mental health" is not particularly helpful. The idea that this type or that type of behavior is healthy or unhealthy I think obscures rather than clarifies the problem. If one accepts the ideas of Thomas Szasz, in his book *The Myth of Mental Illness* and those of Eric Berne in *Games People Play*, among others, one can arrive at a better understanding of the problems of living from the game concept than from the health-sickness concept. In general, I have found this approach more helpful in dealing with parents and children than discussing unconscious motivations, instinctual drives, Oedipus complexes, and castration fears.

Mental illness does not exist at all in the same sense that liver illness exists. Often people say of someone, "he is sick," when they really mean that they do not like the way he behaves. If there is a game of life, and most of the time there is, one that we are required to play, there are rules to the games and players with prescribed roles. We can redefine mental illness, with this model in mind, as those difficulties that arise when one has trouble playing a particular role or when one cannot follow the rules of the game.

A ten-year-old boy who has never been taught to do things for himself, but has gotten things done at home by whining, is in real difficulty with his playmates if he adopts the same demanding, dependent role with them. Worse yet if it works somehow with a few selected friends who are willing to play that game with him, he may later attempt the same pattern with his wife and be somewhat shocked by the results. A role that may work very well in the home when you are five may fail utterly at school when you are seven.

A boy taught only to play soccer may have some adjustment difficulty if he is required to play tennis, the more so if he insists on playing soccer on the tennis court. Sometimes a sudden change in the rules for living, to which it is very hard to adapt, may cause a "psychological breakdown." The rate of mental illness reached epidemic proportions among Bantus in South Africa when they were transported to work in the diamond mines. This problem was somewhat muddily expressed in suitable jargon by a social worker describing the difficulties of an adolescent in our clinic. "She was suffering," the social worker wrote, "from those effects resultant from economic deprivation, social disadvantages, and cultural shock." I asked the social worker if I would change the sense of what she had written if I described our patient as a poor Puerto Rican arriving in New York. If one stops to think about what is going on, forgetting the jargon, defining the problem is not so difficult. The solution is another matter.

If one accepts the game model as being workable, one can see that psychotherapy is more akin to pedagogy than it is to medicine. The therapist is a person who *teaches* the patient, and here I include the parents as well as the child patient, that there are alternatives to the particular behavior that is causing the difficulties. He may change the players, the house rules, or in some instances the game that they are trying to play. An example of the latter would be, for example, asking the parents to remove a child from a school with particularly high academic standards to a technical school, if he feels the child cannot play the "Academic Game." Obviously a careful assessment of the strengths and weaknesses of the players in terms of the demands of the game are extremely important before making changes. In the advanced course, one can learn when games are not necessary—when intimacy and spontaneity have their place. Often when other difficulties are resolved, the latter qualities emerge. I guess in one sense we can all use "psychotherapy."

Anyone visiting a tennis club can see quite readily that almost anyone can improve his game. Even the pros take lessons. Those in most urgent need are the players who do not know the rules or cannot hit the ball.

In a sense, who needs psychotherapy is a matter of priorities. Just as a good tennis instructor analyzes what you are doing, and may or may not correct you, so a psychotherapist does the same except that we say he gives us insight.

There are, of course, many poor tennis players who improve without professional help. One way or the other, they learn the game. So it seems to be in the game of life. The British psychologist Eysenk found that about two-thirds of over eight thousand patients diagnosed as neurotic recovered or improved over a two-year period, regardless of whether they received either formal psychotherapy or medical counseling and advice. Dr. Stella Chess, an eminent child psychiatrist, states that the vast majority of the children referred to her do not need prolonged psychotherapy, but can benefit from guidance. No matter what, we all have problems in everyday living. Children are no exception.

Let me cite a few of the problems that children might have that I find have a good chance of solution.

I have found that almost all toilet-training difficulties resolve themselves. Sleep problems, particularly during the first two years, usually correct themselves. Tics or habit spasms do not, in children, have serious implications in terms of "mental health," if you insist on using that term. Most school phobias, refusal of a bright, conscientious child to go to school, can be handled with good results by parents, teachers, and physician, without psychotherapy.

I hope that nothing I have written is construed to mean that there is not a time and place for psychotherapy. I have written what I have because I have found a change in attitude toward psychotherapy in the past five to ten years. In the late forties and early fifties it was necessary to teach people that there was no stigma attached to seeing a psychiatrist and that there were benefits to be had. In contrast, lately I find that in some circles going to a psychiatrist is a status thing and that people have to be taught that it is no panacea for the problems involved in child-rearing.

In general, one needs the help of a therapist if one has consistent or worsening trouble in one of the numerous games we are required to play in life. A child who can play child to Mama but even with time cannot play the "peer game"—cannot have friends or is always fighting or is chronically seclusive—needs help. A child and mother who have not established a good relationship in the mother-child role, as manifested by constant friction, bickering, and interminable dissonance, need help. Perhaps the mother has to be taught the mother role, or how to respond to a difficult child with unique characteristics.

If your child has a problem that is getting worse rather than better, help is indicated. The child of two who starts out with severe temper tantrums, which is quite common, who worsens in this regard rather than improves so that by the time he is five he has to be hauled squealing and kicking out of a store when he is refused a toy, may need at least an evaluation. The adolescent who persists in meaningless, destructive rebellion, such as refusing to go to school, or refusing to bathe, or uses drugs or alcohol as a reflection of that rebellion, needs psychiatric help.

We all need help in one way or another. There used to be a time when help didn't mean psychiatric help. Helping a child to adjust to the realities of living, of learning to live with himself and with other people, is the chief function of a parent. Or have we all forgotten that?

1001 WAYS PARENTS GET GRAY
A Topographical Approach
to Things That Can Go Wrong

Many parents, after having experienced an emergency caused by an injury, ingestion of a poison, or some acute inflammation or bite, will say, "This kid will be the death of me yet." This chapter is designed as a survival kit for both parent and child. If an emergency arises, the first thing to do is localize it, and then refer to the appropriate section in this chapter, which is organized as follows: Skin, Head, Eyes, Nose, Ears, Mouth, Neck, Chest, Abdomen, Genitals, Extremities.

SKIN

Cuts

The first thing to do for a cut is to stop the bleeding. Cuts in the scalp, even superficial ones, bleed extensively. First find out where the blood is coming from and apply direct pressure to the area with a clean—it need not be sterile—towel, handkerchief, or cloth. Direct pressure will usually stop most bleeding even if the cut is fairly deep.

If an artery is cut, it will spurt. If it's on the head, direct pressure is all you can do until you get to the emergency room. If it's on an extremity, fashion a tourniquet above the site of the injury and tie it, remembering to release it for a few seconds every few minutes to prevent closing off the blood supply.

After the bleeding is stopped, apply a simple antiseptic such as merthiolate or an antibiotic cream or rubbing alcohol (it stings) or plain soap and water. Do the best you can. Remember, doctors don't worry so much about infection and "blood poisoning" since the advent of antibiotics; parents shouldn't either.

Cuts caused by objects that have been lying in the dirt or out of doors call for tetanus immunization.

Bites

INSECT BITES

There are two reactions to a bite, local and general. *Local reactions* are by far the most common and never serious. By local reaction I mean that there is swelling and/or redness at the site of the bites or bite. A cool application of a paste made by mixing a small amount of bicarbonate of soda with water is helpful. If this is not available, application of cold water or ice will ameliorate the pain. If it's a bee sting, try to remove the stinger. Its continued presence, however, is no cause for alarm.

General reactions: two kinds of generalized reactions can occur:

Welts or hives: this reaction following a bite means that your child is sensitive to the toxin of the insect that bit him. Take your child to the nearest doctor or emergency room. If you can get hold of an antihistamine (the medicine used to relieve the symptoms of allergies, such as hay fever), give the child some. A dose for a child over two would be about half the adult dose. Even if you give a little more, the worst that can happen is a little drowsiness. The main point here, however, is to seek medical attention immediately.

Breathing trouble following a bite: the most serious, but fortunately rare, response to an insect bite is breathing difficulty. Usually it's wheezing. If this happens, first fashion a tourniquet above the site of the bite if on the arms or legs to prevent more toxin from getting into the system. Then get to an emergency room or doctor's office as fast as you can. If this is impossible, try to get a nurse or first aid person to administer some adrenalin immediately.

SPIDER BITES

The bite of the black widow spider can cause serious difficulty and even death. It is a small black spider with a red mark shaped like an hour glass on its chest. The black widow has been reported in various parts of this country. Its favorite haunt is in a damp cellar or in an outdoor latrine. For this reason bites on the genitalia are quite common. The bite itself is accompanied by severe burning at the site, and it is often followed by prostration and severe abdominal pain which can be confused with acute appendicitis. In many communities of the South a physician will automatically think of a black widow spider bite when presented with a child with severe abdominal pain. A child suspected of having been bitten by a black widow spider should be seen by a doctor immediately.

ANIMAL BITES

The most important thing to do is to identify and, if possible, catch the animal. The reason for this is to make sure that the animal does not have rabies. The greatest source of rabies in this country at the present time is bats. Bites by pet dogs are usually safe because dogs are usually immunized against rabies. If the dog appears sick, however, it must be checked for rabies immediately.

There has not been any rabies in my part of the country (New York) for over twenty years.

Whatever kind of animal is responsible for the bite, report it to your doctor. In addition to the problem of rabies, protection against tetanus is often needed.

Impetigo

Impetigo is a superficial skin infection that scabs and oozes. Most parents are panicked by it. The word itself apparently conjures up images of isolation and quarantine. This is no longer true. Impetigo is not an emergency, is never serious, and is not nearly as contagious as people think. If your child has a rash that puzzles you, have the doctor look at it. Don't try to describe it on the telephone unless you are Truman Capote. The doctor will probably prescribe an antibiotic, either to be applied locally or taken through the mouth.

Prickly Heat

Prickly heat may appear as tiny raised bumps or blisters surrounded by areas of redness or as tiny bumps or blisters surrounded by whitish areas of skin. It is actually a sweat rash and is more common around the neck and shoulders. Heat, the administration of aspirin, or overdressing, all of which can cause sweating, may bring it on. I would recommend patting the skin with witch hazel to cool it, followed by the application of a simple talcum powder. I do not favor cornstarch because starch when mixed with sweat makes an excellent culture for bacteria and thus may cause secondary infection. Heat rash takes quite a while to go away.

Diaper Rash

A red, raw, sometimes blistered area in the region covered by the diaper often involving the penis, particularly the tip, is diaper rash. It is caused by ammonia released from the urine by certain bacteria. Prevention depends on ridding the diapers of these bacteria. This can be accomplished by boiling, which is awkward, or by the addition of some antiseptic to the diaper pail. Borax, one teaspoon to a gallon of water, is effective. Remember to keep the borax in a safe place out of the reach of children. Diaper services all add antiseptics when preparing the diapers.

Yellow unbleached vaseline is very effective and inexpensive in curing the rash. Lassar's Paste, a thick zinc oxide paste, is also effective and inexpensive. When a diaper rash doesn't respond to simple measures after a couple of days, one must think of the possibility of secondary infection caused by bacteria or monilia, the organism that causes thrush.

Sometimes it isn't diaper rash at all but an inflammation of the oil glands, called seborrhea. Remember that. You may be able to one-up your doctor with that suggestion.

Poison Ivy

Inflammation of the skin can result from contact with the oil of the poison ivy leaf. Individuals vary remarkably in their susceptibility to it. If your child has touched the plant, wash the area off quickly with soap and water, preferably yellow laundry soap.

The rash may consist of:

1. Simple redness. Calamine lotion is helpful.
2. Redness and small blisters. Calamine lotion is helpful.
3. Redness, swelling, and oozing. If this occurs do not apply ointments or lotions. This blocks serum that is oozing and makes matters worse. Apply a compress moistened with either plain water or preferably a solution consisting of one tablespoon of Burrow's solution to a quart of water. Apply the wet compress for fifteen to twenty minutes three times a day.

There is no quick cure for poison ivy. I am not convinced that the application of cortisone-containing lotions or ointments is any more effective than calamine lotion. In severe cases where there is marked swelling of the eyes, lips, and face, ACTH or the cortisone steroids may have to be given, either by injection or by mouth as prescribed by your doctor.

Burns

Extensive burns: A burn that covers a large area of the body is a real emergency even though you may not see blistering right away. Do not apply ointments or greasy material to the area. It will only make it hard for the doctor to remove. Get a clean sheet, wrap the child in it and go to the emergency room of the hospital.

Burns involving smaller areas: There are always new methods for the first aid management of burns. The exact procedure is not too important.

First degree burns cause merely redness of the skin. Run cold water over the area. This may relieve the discomfort. In addition, if you have an ointment containing a local anesthetic, you may apply it. No matter what you do, it will hurt for a bit.

Second degree burns produce redness and blistering. It

is best to consult your doctor. If he is not immediately available, there is no harm in applying some antibiotic cream and bandaging it loosely with a sterile dressing. If you have no antibiotic cream, just apply a sterile dressing.

Third degree burns cause blistering and destruction of the supporting tissues beneath the skin surface. It is sometimes hard in the beginning to distinguish between second and third degree burns. Once again consult your doctor. If he is not available, supply an antibiotic cream and/or a sterile dressing.

Do not apply iodine or any antiseptic tinctures to the burned area.

HEAD

Falls

Children are always falling on their heads. The first thing that parents want to know is, "Did he fracture his skull?" It is usually the last thing the doctor wants to know. After all, the skull is simply a case for the brain. If you dropped an egg crate, you would not worry about the crate, you would worry about the eggs inside. In other words, the doctor is not concerned about the skull but about the brain. Following a head injury, first note the state of consciousness of your child. Is he drowsy? Is he out cold? Does he remember what happened to him? If he is drowsy or unconscious or does not remember what happened to him you had best call your doctor. Try to keep the child aroused.

The main reason that we do not want you to let him sleep is not because sleep is harmful—it is not. Rather it is to make sure he is not in a coma. If it is his bedtime, you can let him go off to sleep providing that you stir him every hour or so to make sure he responds and is not in a coma.

Many children vomit immediately after a fall. This is either from the shaking up or from the fright. Vomiting that is delayed is more serious because it can be a sign of hemorrhage in the skull causing pressure on the brain.

Most children who have some alteration in their state of consciousness, such as being dazed or confused or even periods of unconsciousness, usually clear up gradually in a four-hour period. If your child is getting more rather than less drowsy or stuperous as time goes on, this may mean he is bleeding inside. Careful medical observation in such instances is always indicated.

EYES

Foreign Bodies in the Eyes

This is best handled by the doctor. It is perfectly safe, however, to pull the lid by the lashes away from the eye to give the tears a chance to flush the object away.

An eye cup or even a paper cup can be filled with water and held against the eye. Then have the child raise his head so that the water runs over the eye. He will probably blink a few times, and *voilà*, the object often is washed away. I do not recommend use of boric acid. First of all, it is not very effective in preventing infection, and secondly, it is a highly toxic substance. I do not like even to see it in the house. A small amount taken inadvertently can be fatal. Deaths have occurred when large amounts of boric acid have been applied to infants' damaged skin.

Pink Eye

I mention pink eye simply to state that it is not an emergency. If you notice that the white of the eye is red, or that there is a discharge, call your doctor. You need not do this immediately. You can wipe the eye out with boiled water that has been allowed to clear to remove the discharge until it is feasible to contact your doctor.

NOSE

Foreign Bodies in the Nose

Kids put the damnedest things in their noses. Beans and screws, pebbles and marbles are most common. If you can see the object, you can try to remove it with blunt forceps. What would you be doing with blunt forceps? Have the child blow his nose if you think he can without hurting himself. The force may expel the object. If in doubt, have your doctor remove it.

If your child has a persistent discharge from only one nostril, think of the presence of a foreign body. I recently removed a small screw from the left nostril of a child which apparently had been there for two months.

Nosebleeds

A nosebleed in a child is rarely serious. Mostly, it stops of its own accord. The most common type usually occurs at night, frequently from one nostril. Very often a sleeping child will push his finger in his nose and scratch the mucous membrane.

Nosebleed, usually from both nostrils, occurs commonly with any upper respiratory infection or with allergies involving the nose. The following steps are helpful and work most of the time.

First, try to get the child to blow his nose vigorously to get rid of clots. Several droppers of three per cent hydrogen peroxide (the usual strength) or plain tap water should be used to irrigate the nostrils. Next, instill some common nose drops, such as Privine or Neo-synephrine. These cause the blood vessels to constrict. Next apply ice to the back of the neck and over the nose. If all this doesn't work, squeeze the nose tightly between the thumb and forefinger.

All of the above presupposes a certain amount of cooperation. If this is not possible, the following routine may have to be tried. Hold the child's head up. Place an ice cube against the upper lip for one minute. If this doesn't stop the bleeding, you can push a little cotton into BOTH NOSTRILS, making sure the cotton is in firmly. Don't be afraid to pack it in tight. If you happen to have any common nose drops, you may wet the cotton with them before insertion.

EARS

Earaches

Earaches are common from infancy to six or seven years of age. Most but not all earaches follow a stuffy nose because mucous is forced through the Eustachian tube into the middle ear. An infant who cries incessantly while he has a cold should be suspected of having an earache. Older children will hold their ear, or if they can talk, they will complain bitterly. A word of caution. An earache may last an hour or two or disappear. This does not mean that there is no infection. As the drum stretches, the pain ceases.

What to do. Ear drops, which contain a local anesthetic-like substance, are good to have around. If you do not have them, some warm mineral oil or olive oil might be helpful. Heat applied to the ear, in the form of a heating pad or a hot water bottle is also helpful. Aspirin may help relieve the pain. Cough mixtures which contain codeine or codeine-like substances are even more effective. Paregoric, one drop for each two pounds of body weight —no more than a teaspoonful—is also effective.

Most earaches are the result of an infection so that a physician should be called at some reasonable time. It is not, however, an emergency.

MOUTH

Cuts

One of the most frequently injured structures in the mouth is the frenulum. This is the attachment between the upper lip and the gum, in the midportion of the undersurface of the lip. It is frequently torn if the child falls on his face, and it bleeds fairly profusely. The bleeding always stops spontaneously, and it always heals itself. It is best to apply a little pressure to the upper lip for about a minute, releasing and reapplying pressure until the bleeding stops. The frenulum has no important function. It is suggested that children under two not be allowed to play the tuba for a two-week period after injury. Otherwise there are no restrictions.

Another common injury is one in which the lower teeth are pushed through the lower lips. The lower lip splits, rarely widely, and rarely requires a stitch, unless it gapes widely.

Swallowed Objects

When an infant inadvertently swallows an object, there are two places that the object can go. It can either go down the foodpipe, the esophagus, or it can go down the windpipe, the trachea. If the object goes down the esophagus, it will pass into the stomach.

OBJECTS THAT GO INTO THE STOMACH

I have seen the most remarkable objects pass into the stomach, through the intestine, and out the rectum without causing any difficulty at all. I have seen coins, both foreign and domestic; buttons, plastic and pearl; whistles, wooden and tin; and marbles of all shades of the rainbow. The point is that most objects will pass through without getting hung up somewhere. I usually ask the parent to watch the stool for at least a week, to make sure the object comes out. Some objects will show up on X-ray, others will not. Sharp objects, such as open-ended safety pins, have to be watched more carefully.

OBJECTS THAT GO INTO THE WINDPIPE

If, following the swallowing of an object, there is coughing or choking, it may mean that the object has gone down the windpipe and possibly into the lung. If the child is choking, the first thing to do is to turn the child *upside down* and slap him on the back a few times. If there is no immediate relief, start out for the emergency room of the hospital where there is equipment to help immediately.

Tongue

Lacerations of the tongue are very common. The tongue contains many blood vessels and therefore bleeds profusely. It is very difficult to suture (stitch), but very large lacerations often heal without suturing. Your doctor will have to decide.

Thrush

Thrush is a fungous infection common in infants. It

usually appears as a thick white coating that cannot be removed, for example, with the side of a spoon. White spots, also not readily removable, may be seen inside the cheeks. I mention thrush not because it is serious, but because it may be the cause of an infant's refusal to eat. Your physician has a wide variety of medications that are effective against it.

Teeth

If a tooth is knocked out, you might call your dentist. Some dentists try to push the tooth back in its socket in hopes that it will take hold. Sometimes it does. This is particularly true for second teeth.

NECK

Swollen Glands

The two most common causes of swelling in the neck are swollen glands and mumps. See the chapter "What the Heck Are Those Lumps."

Croup

Croup involves the voice box, the larynx, and the structures around it. It is a combination usually of infection and spasm. A typical case of croup starts in a child with a slight cold during the day. Usually quite suddenly, around midnight, the child will suddenly either develop a cough that sounds like a barking seal (you have heard a seal bark) or a harsh loud sound when he breathes. It is often accentuated by crying. Let me emphasize. The noise occurs when the child inhales. This is in contrast to the wheezing in asthma, which usually occurs when the child exhales or when he inhales and exhales both.

Croup is common between six months and two years of age but does occur later. Croup is most often mild, but it can be serious because if there is enough mucous the airway to the lung may be closed off, requiring a tracheotomy. This is an opening in the wind pipe to allow the child to breathe. Elizabeth Taylor, not too long ago, had this operation performed in London. It was not, however, for croup.

What to do for croup: If there seems to be a lot of trouble getting air in, bring the child as soon as possible into a bathroom made steamy by running a hot shower. A vaporizer, I prefer the cold steam vaporizer, is helpful, particularly if the vapors can be collected under a canopy you can fashion by suspending a sheet over the sides of a crib. An open umbrella will work for an older child—if you are not superstitious. By all means call your doctor. He may be able to determine the severity of it by hearing your child breathe over the telephone. In a series of tests, it was found that doctors could be quite accurate about diagnosing and evaluating croup over the phone.

A rare cause of croup is a foreign body in the respiratory passages. If your child has croup or any sort of wheezing, try to remember whether he gagged on something or something went down the wrong pipe. It is rare, but it is important to know.

CHEST

Wheezing

The most common acute chest condition is asthma. Asthma usually starts fairly suddenly. A child will develop a high-pitched wheezing sound first heard on expiration. Start a vaporizer and call the doctor.

A foreign body, such as a peanut down the wrong pipe into the lung, can cause wheezing. If your child chokes on something and this is followed by wheezing, get in touch with your doctor.

Coughs

Coughs associated with fever usually indicate infection in the respiratory tract. It may be anything from upper respiratory infection, nose, throat, larynx, or windpipe, to inflammation in the tubes leading to the lungs—bronchitis —to involvement of the lung itself—pneumonia. A cough with fever should be reported to your doctor.

Breathing Stoppage

This may be the result of drowning, suffocation, electrical shock, or inhaling gas. A person who cannot breathe for himself needs artificial respiration.

Using your finger, wipe the child's mouth clear of mucous, vomit, food, gum, or foreign bodies. Turn him over on his back. Tilt the head back by raising the lower jaw with your hands. Apply your mouth to the patient's mouth and blow. If you are doing it correctly, the patient's chest should rise as you breathe air into his lungs. If this doesn't happen check his mouth again to make sure there is nothing there preventing the air from going down his windpipe into his lungs. If nothing is to be seen, lift the child up by his ankles and strike him sharply between the shoulders. If he is too heavy, turn him on his side and strike him between the shoulder blades. Start the mouth to mouth breathing again.

ABDOMEN

Appendicitis

By far the most common abdominal emergency in a child is an inflamed appendix. The usual story is one in which the child first indicates he has abdominal pain. This is usually followed by vomiting. It rarely starts with vomiting. Following the vomiting, the pain usually starts again. There may be little or no fever. The pain usually does not start on the right side but rather in the middle. It may never localize on the right side. The child usually has not had a bowel movement that day. Diarrhea accompanying it is rare but not unknown. As you can see, an acute appendicitis is very difficult to diagnose. Even the blood count may not be helpful.

If your child has persistent abdominal pain for more than an hour, call your doctor. An acute appendicitis usually takes hours to develop, so do not panic. There are those that rupture at the onset because there is a calcium deposit blocking the appendix, but this is very rare and cannot be prevented unless the doctor happens to see the calcium deposit on an X-ray.

Most doctors do not believe in chronic appendicitis; so if your child has occasional pains usually around the "belly button," not associated with vomiting, do not panic; it is not appendicitis. It should be investigated anyway, but it can be done more leisurely.

Again let me emphasize, persistent abdominal pain is a problem for a physician. Do not administer enemas; this can rupture the affected appendix. For the same reason, do not give a laxative.

GENITALS

Hernias

I have discussed umbilical hernias, which are rarely troublesome, on page 27. Hernias in the region of the groin are the ones that cause the most concern. If you notice a lump in the groin area that comes and goes, report it to your doctor. The hernia will usually appear when the child is crying or straining. The doctor may have to have the child blow up a balloon in order to see the hernia. If the child is too young to blow up a balloon, the doctor may have to make him cry.

These hernias do not get better spontaneously and are not helped by trusses. Until it is surgically repaired, there is always the risk that the hernia will become caught outside and become strangulated. That is why surgery as soon as feasible, no matter what the age of the child, is strongly recommended.

Testicles

A rare but important emergency to know about is a twisted testicle. This usually occurs spontaneously and is called torsion of the testicle. It is manifested by acute onset of pain and tenderness in the region of the testicle. See a doctor immediately. A testicle that remains twisted may get gangrene and have to be removed.

For treatment of undescended testicles, see page 146.

Hydrocele

Hydrocele is Greek for bag of water. It means a collection of fluids, most often around the testicle, less frequently in the groin. It is very often present in the newborn period. Most of these disappear spontaneously. They, themselves, are harmless. The major problem is to distinguish them from hernia. Occasionally hydroceles located in the groin are the forerunner of hernias. The main point to remember is that if you note a swelling in the groin or testicle, particularly if it comes and goes, report it to your doctor. It may not be visible when he examines the child.

The Child Who Will Not Urinate

The most common reason that infants and children will not urinate is the presence of a sore either on the tip of the penis near the opening, or in girls near the opening of the urethra, the short passage coming out of the bladder. It is far more common in boys, where the opening of the urethra is easily irritated, usually by rubbing against the wet diaper. In any event the opening of the urethra either in boys or girls can get so irritated that urine passing over it causes much pain. The child, therefore, holds back. I have found two steps helpful in this situation. First, put the child in a warm tub. This usually soothes the area of the urethral opening and relaxes the child, and he probably will urinate. Be prepared to duck. Usually a simple antibiotic cream applied to the area will have excellent healing results.

If putting a child in a warm tub does not get him to urinate, an investigation by your doctor is necessary.

I do not think that I need to tell you that an infant who urinates blood or a smoky-colored urine should have a medical evaluation.

Vaginal Discharge

It is common. Very often and quite normally in a newborn girl there may be a thick whitish discharge that can persist for a week. I say quite normally because it is the normal response to the female hormones, which, during the last part of pregnancy, have crossed from the mother's circulation to the baby's through the placenta. These hormones cause the discharge. Since the infant does not produce any hormones of its own, the discharge soon passes away.

Vaginal discharge is also quite common in older children, particularly in the period just before adolescence. It is usually thin and watery looking. If it causes burning, have the child take a warm "sitz bath," that is, a shallowly filled tub to which about four tablespoons of bicarbonate of soda are added.

A thicker pus discharge needs medical attention. Temporarily, a sitz bath to which has been added some liquid antiseptic soap, such as Phiso Hex, may be helpful.

If the vaginal discharge is persistent, thick, foul-smelling, or particularly if it contains blood, the possibility of a foreign body in the vagina must be considered. Do not be embarrassed; it can happen to anybody's kid.

EXTREMITIES

Fractures

Most children break a bone at some time or other. A fall that results in pain, swelling, often a black and blue mark, and some limitation of motion should be evaluated by a doctor. Children's fractures are usually easier to repair than adults', if that is any compensation.

If it appears that your child has broken an arm or leg, try to move it as little as possible. Splint the arm or leg with rolled up newspaper or a wooden board, fastening it so as to prevent motion, and get medical care.

Fractures in the arms or legs are usually easy for parents to suspect. But one fracture that I have found that can be overlooked is a fracture of the collarbone. The child may fall on his outstretched hand or on his shoulder and this fairly fragile bone, the collarbone, will bear the force of the blow and crack. Sometimes the break can be felt, but often there is no swelling visible and the fracture can be seen only by X-ray. A child with a fractured collarbone will cry if you pick him up or if he has to raise his arms.

A fracture of the toes or small bones of the foot may also be painful and have no outward sign. Like the fracture of the collarbone, an X-ray may be the only way of discovering it.

Nursemaid's Elbow

This is obviously an anachronistic name since practically no one has a nursemaid any more. It is a temporary dislocation of the elbow caused by yanking the child's arm, usually as you are crossing the street. The arm will hang limp and the child will cry if you try to bend it. Your doctor can usually easily snap it into place. Push the child, do not pull him across the street. Better yet, yell at him.

Sprains

I don't know why, but it seldom fails that when a child falls after twisting his ankle, there is someone around who runs over and shouts, "Make him walk on it." Nine chances out of ten, he is called "Doc," and a scrutiny of his credentials will reveal that he earned this eponym by having taken a first aid course in high school or by being the son of a pharmacist. My own advice is quite the contrary. If you have injured yourself by twisting your ankle or your knee or falling on your wrist, move it around as little as possible. In the first place, there may be a fracture. In the second place, if it is not fractured, it is likely to be sprained.

What is a sprain? A sprain is a pulling of a muscle, a ligament, or the capsule, the protective tissue that surrounds a joint. A sprain is likely to be accompanied by pain and swelling. Occasionally it may become black and blue. It is often difficult to distinguish a sprain from a fracture without an X-ray.

The best thing to do is to move the affected part as little as possible, elevate it, and apply an ice bag. Remember, by the way, to keep the ice bag on for five minutes and off for five minutes. Your child can get frost bite from an ice bag applied too long. What does he need frost bite for? He already has a sprain.

If there is swelling or pain on motion, it is best to consult a physician.

POISONS,
A GUIDE TO EMERGENCIES

1. If you think your child has ingested a potentially poisonous substance, the first thing to be done is to identify it. If it was in a can or a bottle try to ascertain from the label what the contents are. If there is no label you should save some of the substance so that it may be identified later.

2. Phone your physician or a hospital emergency room. In many cities there are Poison Control Centers, which may be reached by phone and are available to both you and your physician for emergency advice.

3. If a physician or any of the above facilities is not immediately available, the first decision you will have to make is whether to induce vomiting or not.

4. *When not to induce vomiting:*
   a. If the child is drowsy or unconscious.
   b. If he is convulsing or has taken some medication that might cause convulsions before you can induce vomiting.
   c. If the substance ingested is corrosive. Common corrosive substances: ammonia—bleaches—carbolic acid—disinfectants—corn or wart removers—drain cleaners—lye—oven cleaners—rust removers—strong acids, such as hydrochloric acid, sulfuric acid, nitric acid—strong alkalies such as sodium hydroxide—Drano—styptic pencil—toilet bowl cleaners—washing soda.
   d. If a petroleum product has been ingested, such as: benzene—kerosene—brush cleaners—lighter fluids—furniture polish—paint thinner—gasoline—tur-

pentine—grease removers—typewriter cleaner—
—gun cleaner—wood preservative.

5. *When to induce vomiting:* In most other instances
vomiting is the best way to start the treatment of poisoning.
I emphasize *start* because even if vomiting has been in-
duced, medical care should be sought. Some poisons have a
delayed effect. Aspirin, for example, may not cause serious
symptoms for many hours after it has been taken.

6. *How to induce vomiting:* I suggest that you obtain
from your druggist one ounce of syrup of ipecac—I repeat
syrup—and keep it in the medicine cabinet for emergencies. It is a good idea to write the telephone number of
your doctor and your nearest Poison Control Center on the
label in case you need to check as to whether to induce
vomiting or not.

For a child over one year of age, if vomiting is advised,
administer one tablespoon of syrup of ipecac. Follow this,
if possible, with large amounts of water. If vomiting has
not occurred in twenty minutes, give the remainder of the
syrup of ipecac in the one-ounce bottle. This is, again, approximately one tablespoonful. If there is no vomiting
after this, it is important that the stomach be evacuated by
other means. This will probably have to be done by your
doctor with a stomach pump.

A good procedure to follow is to administer the first
dose of syrup of ipecac and then start for the emergency
ward with towels and a bucket or basin to collect the vom-
itus.

If you do not have syrup of ipecac, give the child some
carbonated beverage and follow this immediately with an
attempt to cause vomiting by tickling the back of the
throat with the blunt end of a spoon handle or with your
finger.

7. The following is a list of common household poisons
with suggestions for their management.

*Alcohol, ethyl or isopropyl (alcoholic beverages or rub-
bing alcohol).* Usually mild cases need no special
care. Induce vomiting, and consult with physician.

Alcohol, methyl. Induce vomiting and call a physician.

Alkalies: caustic soda, lye, Drano. Do not cause vomiting.
Give large doses of water containing vinegar, lemon
juice, or other citrus fruits. Follow with milk, salad
oil, or olive oil. Call the doctor.

Ammonia: ammonia water, solution of ammonia. Do not

cause vomiting. Treat as above for alkalies. Consult physician immediately.

Amphetamines. Cause vomiting; call your physician.

Antihistamines (drugs used for allergy). There are no specific antidotes. Induce vomiting; follow with tea or coffee to prevent drowsiness. Call your physician.

Antifreeze. Induce vomiting. Call your physician.

APC tablets. See headache remedies.

Argyrol. See silver preparations.

Arsenic. Offer milk and then induce vomiting. Contact your physician immediately, and start out for the emergency room.

Aspirin. Induce vomiting. The effects of aspirin can be delayed for many hours; therefore close observation is essential.

Atropine. See belladonna alkaloids.

Barbiturates: Phenobarbital, Nembutal, Seconal, Veronal. If patient is not drowsy, induce vomiting. Call your physician.

Belladonna alkaloids: tincture of belladonna, atropine, hyoscamine. Induce vomiting, contact your physician, and go to the emergency room.

Benzedrine. Induce vomiting. Call your physician.

Benzene: benzol, toluene, xylene. If inhaled, remove the patient to fresh air as soon as possible. If ingested, do *not* induce vomiting. Call your doctor.

Benzine. See petroleum products.

Benzol. See benzene.

Birth control pills. Not very toxic. If more than three pills are ingested, it is probably best to induce vomiting.

Boric acid. Highly toxic. Cause vomiting immediately. Call doctor.

Bufferin. See headache remedies.

Caffergot. See ergot.

Camphor: camphorated oil. Induce vomiting. Call doctor.

Carbon dioxide gas. Remove patient to fresh air. Oxygen therapy is desirable if available.

Carbon monoxide gas. This usually occurs from automobile exhaust fumes, particularly if the exhaust system is defective. It may happen in the back of a car or station wagon. The child may become cherry red in color. Remove immediately to fresh air. Give oxygen if available.

Carbon tetrachloride. If inhaled, remove to fresh air. If ingested, do not induce vomiting. Call your physician and go to the emergency room.

Cathartics (laxatives). Induce vomiting. Call your physician.

Caustic soda. See alkalies.

Chloral hydrates. Induce vomiting immediately. Call your physician.

Chlorpromazine. See tranquilizers.

Cigarettes. As little as the tobacco from one cigarette can be harmful. Induce vomiting. Call doctor.

Cleaning fluids. Do not induce vomiting. Call your doctor.

Codeine. Many cough mixtures contain codeine or codeinelike substances to stop coughing. Induce vomiting. Have child observed for unusual drowsiness. Remember, do not induce vomiting if child is very drowsy or unconscious.

Corrosives: mineral acids, sulfuric acid, hydrochloric acid (muriatic acid), glacial acetic acid. Do not cause vomiting. If an alkali such as milk of magnesia is available, administer it or offer plenty of milk to neutralize the acid. Call your physician and go to the emergency room.

Crayons. Cause vomiting. The dyes in crayons can be toxic, causing the blood to become bluish (methemoglobinemia). Call your physician.

Cuticle remover. Induce vomiting. Follow with milk or the white of an egg in the milk or mixed with water or, if these are not available, a teaspoonful of olive oil. Call your physician.

Cyanides. Induce vomiting, and start out for the emergency room.

DDT. Induce vomiting. Call your physician.

Demerol. See meperidine hydrochloride.

Dipilatory preparations (hair removers). Give Epsom salts, and follow by vomiting. If you have no Epsom salts, simply induce vomiting. Call your physician.

Detergents, powder or liquid. Most are not caustic but are mildly alkaline. Offer orange juice to neutralize and then induce vomiting. Call your physician.

Dexamil. Cause vomiting. Call your physician.

Dexedrine. Cause vomiting. Call your physician.

Digitalis: digitoxin, digoxin. Induce vomiting, and call your physician.

Dolantine, Dolantol. See meperidine hydrochloride.

Drano. See alkalies.

Equanil. See tranquilizers.

Ergot: ergotamine, caffergot, etc. Induce vomiting, and call your physician.

Fingernail polish. Induce vomiting, and call your physician.

Gasoline. See petroleum products.

Hair removers. See depilatory preparations.

Hair-waving lotions, home permanents. Treat as you would for caustics. Do not induce vomiting.

Headache remedies: aspirin, Bufferin, APC tablets. Induce vomiting. Remember that the effects of aspirin poisoning may be delayed many hours so keep the child under observation.

Herbicides. See pest control poisons.

Hyoscamine. See belladonna alkaloids.

Hyoscine (scopolamine). Induce vomiting. Call your physician.

Iodine. Administer plenty of water and starch or flour. You may then induce vomiting. After vomiting give the white of an egg or milk or both together. Call your physician.

Iron preparations or tablets. Contrary to popular belief these can be dangerous. Induce vomiting and call your physician.

Kerosene. See petroleum products.

Laxatives. See cathartics.

Lead or lead solutions. This is not to be confused with the lead in a lead pencil which is harmless. Induce vomiting. You may follow the vomiting with Epsom salts. Call your physician.

Librium. See tranquilizers.

Lye. See alkalies.

Meperidine hydrochloride: Demerol, Dolantin, Dolantol. Induce vomiting. Call your physician.

Meprobamate. See tranquilizers.

Mercury: metallic mercury. Taken in small quantities this is not harmful. Usually children get a very small amount from a broken thermometer. You may give a very simple laxative such as milk of magnesia or mineral oil.

Miltown. See tranquilizers.

Mothballs. Induce vomiting. Call doctor.

Naphtha. See petroleum products.

Nembutal. See barbiturates.

Nicotine. The very small amount of tobacco that children usually swallow is not harmful. Large amounts, such as a whole cigarette, may be harmful, however, and a few drops of plant spray containing nicotine may be harmful. Therefore, if in doubt it is best to induce vomiting and contact your doctor.

Niter. See potassium nitrate.

Pep pills. See amphetamine, Benzedrine, Dexamil, Dexedrine.

Pest control poisons: herbicides, insecticides, pesticides, rodenticides. Unless they are known to contain harsh alkalies or acids as stated on the container, induce vomiting, then give milk. These substances are very dangerous and care in the emergency room by a physician should be sought.

Petroleum products: kerosene, gasoline, naphtha, benzine. Do not induce vomiting. Give milk and/or two tablespoons of mineral or vegetable oil.

Phenobarbital. See barbiturates.

Potassium nitrate: saltpeter, niter. Induce vomiting. Call your physician.

Quinine. Induce vomiting, and call your physician.

Reserpine. See tranquilizers.

Rodenticides. See pest control poisons.

Saltpeter. See potassium nitrate.

Scopolamine. Induce vomiting. Call your physician.

Seconal. See barbiturates.

Silver preparations: silver nitrate, argyrol. Give one teaspoon of salt water to children above two, one-half teaspoon to one-year-olds, and one-third teaspoon to children under one (large amounts of salt given to infants are dangerous). Follow by vomiting.

Strychnine nux vomica. An emetic may only be used within a few minutes of ingestion since strychnine may cause convulsions, and a convulsing child may choke on his vomit. If there is any doubt about the time of ingestion, do not cause vomiting. Call your physician.

Thallium. Offer milk, and then induce vomiting.

Thorazine. See tranquilizers.

Toluene. See benzene.

Tranquilizers: Chlorpromazine, Equanil, Librium, Meprobamate, Miltown, Reserpine, Thorazine. Induce vomiting if within a few minutes of ingestion. Tranquilizers can cause convulsions or drowsiness. If in any doubt about the time of ingestion, do not cause vomiting. Start for the emergency room.

Turpentine. Do not induce vomiting. Give several ounces of milk and/or two tablespoons of mineral or vegetable oil.

Veronal. See barbiturates.

Wintergreen, oil of. Toxic effects are similar to aspirin, but it is highly concentrated. Induce vomiting immediately. Call your physician.

Xylene. See benzene.

AND HOW DOES YOUR GARDEN GROW?

It is not commonly know that many common house, garden and field plants are poisonous. I am indebted to Dr. Ara Der Maderosian for his compilation as it appeared in the *Current Medical Digest,* condensed from the *American Journal of Pharmaceutical Education.*

The following is a partial list of the various potentially poisonous plants and the emergency treatment. If your child has been eating a plant that you cannot identify, save it and contact your doctor, the emergency room of your hospital, or a poison control center.

House and Garden Plants

Castor Bean. All parts are toxic, but mainly the seed. Call your doctor or poison control center, or go to the emergency room.

Christmas rose. The rootstocks and leaves are toxic. Induce vomiting and call your doctor or poison control center, or go to the emergency room.

Foxglove. The leaves and seeds are toxic. Induce vomiting, and call the doctor or poison control center, or go to the emergency room.

Hyacinth. The bulb is toxic. Induce vomiting and call the doctor.

Iris or blue flag. The toxic parts are the leaves and the rootstocks. Call your doctor or poison control center, or go to the emergency room.

Lily of the valley. The toxic parts are the leaves, flowers, and roots. Call the doctor or poison control center, or go to the emergency room.

Narcissus or daffodil. The toxic part is the bulb. Call the doctor or poison control center, or go to the emergency room.

Poinsettia. The toxic part is the juice of the leaves, stems, flowers, or the fruit whether dry or green. Offer plenty of milk—a glass or two—and/or mineral or vegetable oil. Call the doctor or poison control center, or go to the emergency room.

Vegetable Garden

Potato. The toxic parts are the green "sun-burned" spots and sprouts of potato tubers, green stems, and leaves. Induce vomiting, call doctor.

Rhubarb. The toxic part is the leaf blade, not the leaf stem which is edible. Give milk and induce vomiting. Call the doctor or go to the emergency room.

Ornamental Plants

Lantana. The toxic parts are the berries. Induce vomiting. Call the doctor or poison control center, or go to the emergency room.

Mountain laurel. All parts are toxic. Call the doctor or poison control center, or go to the emergency room.

Wisteria. Seeds or pods are toxic. Induce vomiting. Call the doctor or poison control center, or go to the emergency room.

Trees and Shrubs

Cherries, wild or cultivated. Toxic parts are the twigs and leaves. Call the doctor or poison control center, or go to the emergency room.

Field Plants

Buttercup. All of it is toxic, especially the juice. Give one or two glasses of milk and/or vegetable or mineral oil. Call the doctor or poison control center, or go to the emergency room.

Jimson weed or thorn apple. All parts are poisonous, especially the seeds. Call the doctor or poison control center, or go to the emergency room.

Poison hemlock. The leaves, stem, and fruit are toxic. Call the doctor or poison control center, or go to the emergency room.

Mistletoe. The toxic part is the berry. Induce vomiting. Call the doctor or poison control center, or go to the emergency room.

Poisonous Plants in Wooded Areas

Moonseed. Toxic parts are the roots and fruit. The plant resembles a grape vine and may be mistaken for it. Call the doctor or poison control center, or go to the emergency room.

Snake berry or bane berry. Toxic parts are the berries, rootstock and sap. Induce vomiting. Call the doctor or poison control center, or go to the emergency room.

Unidentified mushrooms. All parts may be toxic. Induce vomiting. Call the doctor or poison control center, or go to the emergency room.

SAY BYE-BYE TO THE DOCTOR

I have seen some very independent people utterly dependent on a baby book. "I don't make a move without consulting Spock." I hope the readers of this book feel free to make a move, in fact live their lives without consulting Gersh at every turn. I see as my role, both as pediatrician and as the author of this book, to make myself as dispensable as possible. I've had my say and it boils down to a comparatively few points.

Our society pays a great deal of attention to such matters as breast-feeding, pro and con, and toilet-training, this month or next. What the evidence we have on hand shows is that it doesn't really matter. I've tried to include what does matter in this book, the danger symptoms to watch for (they are really few), the realities of child care (as opposed to the "psychological realities," many of which are theories that come and go), and so on. I have tried to emphasize an attitude towards child care that will enable a parent to relax about being a parent while getting junior on his feet.

In Western society, children were not always set apart from adults as they are now. Once upon a time there were no special games for children, no special kiddie clothing; as soon as children were old and strong enough, they worked alongside of adults. In our own time, the concept of childhood has become embroidered with so much worrisome effort and anxiety-ridden psychologizing, that child-rearing has become a full-time, energy and soul-consuming obsession instead of a way of helping a child get through childhood with a minimum of pain for the parent as well as the child. We may now be coming to recognize that genetic

185

influences and social forces play so large a part in the fate of our children that the areas we can control are rather limited. I have tried to focus on those areas.

Like thousands of other pediatricians I have heard a mother say "But it says in Dr. Spock. . . ." I feel, as many of my colleagues do, that when Dr. Spock wrote his book and left his practice, in a sense he left us holding the baby.

Of course, Spock is amazingly complete. In some sense it is too complete. In the chapter on "The Tub Bath," Dr. Spock suggests as step number one before starting the bath, "Take off your wrist watch." I am for the independent mother. If she wants to soak her wrist watch, let her. If she doesn't know enough to take it off, I can't help her.

Mothers who read this book and go along with my approach may very well suffer from wet wrist watches, but maybe they'll enjoy motherhood a bit more.

I remember when the father of a patient of mine said, "I like you a lot, Doc, but I hope I don't see you too soon." That's fine with me.

INDEX